exploring america

Quiz and Exam Book

answer key

Ray Notgrass

exploring america
Quiz and Exam Book
Answer Key

Ray Notgrass

Notgrass Company
370 S. Lowe Avenue, Suite A
PMB 211
Cookeville, Tennessee 38501

1-800-211-8793
books@notgrass.com
www.notgrass.com

Published in the United States by the Notgrass Company.

Unit 1

Lesson 1

1. History is our story; history helps us understand the present; history helps us learn from the past; God teaches us that history is important.
2. We are descendants of immigrants; we are influenced by the section of the country in which we live; we are children and grandchildren of people who lived during the Great Depression, the Cold War, etc.
3. We are ennobled by those who have done good and convicted by those who have done wrong.
4. It reminds us that the ideas and assumptions people have today are not the only ones possible, and perhaps they are not even good ideas and assumptions.
5. They are condemned to repeat it.
6. They both have stood for ideas that are out of the mainstream.
7. Moses' speeches to the Israelites in Deuteronomy before they entered the Promised Land; Joshua's speech to the Israelites after they had conquered the Promised Land; the Levites' prayer after the captives had returned from Babylon; Stephen's defense before the Jewish authorities
8. To help them remember and honor their past
9. At a definite time and place in history
10. We can see how God has worked and is working today for our good, fulfilling His plan.

Questions on "Knowing History and Knowing Who We Are"

1. People never think of themselves as living in the past. Everyone lives in the present—their present.
2. That all of the thirteen original colonies were on the east coast
3. We have to know who we were.
4. At home
5. For him to turn out to be a blockhead with all of the opportunities he had had

Lesson 2

1. Expansion, power and control, a mixture of good and evil, ethnocentricity, the fabric of history
2. Geographic expansion, expansion of personal rights, cultural and intellectual expansion (taking in people from different cultural backgrounds, adopting new ideas)

3. As America has expanded, Native Americans have suffered loss; slaves were abused to help others; the U.S. has borne a cost in money and lives as our influence has spread around the world.
4. Puritans wanted to control their community; whites have wanted to control blacks; political parties and candidates want power to be able to control government.
5. Individuals have done good and bad things; developments such as industrialization have brought positive and negative consequences.
6. The tendency of a people to see themselves and their ways as better than others
7. The events of history are intertwined and affect later events.
8. We see the same kind of issues emerge time after time.
9. Every situation is unique in some way.
10. God chose Israel; and then God chose Christians. God has blessed the U.S., but we have no similar Divine revelation that He has chosen the U.S. as His special people in the same way.

Lesson 3

1. Continuity
2. The Roman Catholic Church
3. They accepted it.
4. It changed from seeing the accepted order of things as God's will to seeing the search for new possibilities as God's will.
5. Renaissance
6. They introduced the cultures, lands, and riches of the East to Europe.
7. The desire for greater trade with countries of the East
8. It is traditionally thought that they crossed over a land bridge at the Bering Strait that no longer exists. More recent theories suggest the possibility that they came by boat.
9. Aztec
10. Forces that cause people movements. Push forces (such as war and famine) drive people out of their homelands, while pull forces (such as the desire for conquest or riches) pull people to new lands.

Lesson 4

1. Spain
2. He thought the earth was smaller than it is, and he didn't count on another continent lying

between Europe and Asia

3. The division of the world into two spheres that Spain and Portugal could explore freely

4. Magellan

5. Cortes

6. St. Augustine

7. To control the region; to extract gold and other riches and send them back to Spain; to find a water route to Asia

8. Spain

9. Leif Ericson

10. Europeans picked up some Native American terms and became familiar with some crops grown by the Native Americans. More importantly, Native Americans were taught the gospel; but they were also decimated by diseases and wars of conquest that the Europeans brought.

Bible Questions

1. Europeans should have had their awareness raised about other people they had not known about who needed to learn about Christ. They also should have realized that the world was much bigger and more complex than they had thought.

2. Europeans did not have a right to conquer lands in the western hemisphere. This was something they assumed.

3. Europeans did not have the right to impose their way of life on Native Americans, although they should have shared ways that were improvements over what the Native Americans knew.

4. If European Christians had shown a willingness to accept and learn from Native Americans, the Native Americans might have been more willing to learn the gospel from the Europeans.

Lesson 5

1. A person's understanding of the world in which he or she lives: where it came from, its purpose, and how he or she fits in it

2. Beliefs, experiences, cultural training, family background, political orientation, ideals, belief (or lack of belief) in God

3. People who believe in God versus those who believe in gods; materialistic views versus belief in the supernatural; a cyclical view of history versus a view that life and history have a purpose and are headed for a conclusion

4. Protestants might see it as a positive event while Catholics might see it as a tragedy.

5. Some might see it as an attempt by people to gain their legitimate rights, while others might see it as a subversive Communist plot.

6. Whether someone should have an abortion; the responsibility people have to care for the earth; whether a dad should take a challenging promotion that will cost his family significantly

7. Answers will vary, but they might include Pearl Harbor, the September 11, 2001 terrorist attacks, participation in war, or personal loss (such as experiencing an abortion or having a daughter experience one).

8. Belief that God made the world and sustains it, that man is specially created in God's image, that God is guiding the events of history, that all should be done to honor Christ, that God has given us standards of right and wrong, that all people will stand before God in final judgment, and that God's ultimate will will be accomplished

9. The story of what happened in the past, and an interpretation of what happened in the past

10. He spoke of things they knew, addressed questions they had, and even quoted from a pagan poet.

11. He told them about the God they did not know and told them about the One whom God had raised from the dead.

Questions on "The Meaning of July Fourth for the Negro"

1. He complimented their courage and their willingness to throw off oppression.

2. He saw America as not fulfilling its promise and its principles because slavery was still being practiced. In this sense America was a failure.

3. He criticized their support of slavery.

4. Americans spoke of freedom but kept millions in slavery and denied the personhood of blacks.

5. Because he had been a slave and had seen the cruelties of the slave system

6. The worldview of whites led blacks to be enslaved and to be denied equality.

7. Answers will vary.

History Quiz on Unit 1

1. True; 2. True; 3. False; 4. True; 5. True; 6. True; 7. False; 8. True; 9. False; 10. False; 11. False; 12. True; 13. False; 14. True; 15. False; 16. Rebirth; 17. Gutenberg; 18. Italian; 19. Amerigo Vespucci; 20. St. Augustine

Unit 2

Lesson 6

1. The Roman Catholic Church was a wealthy, powerful institution that exerted considerable influence over kings and politics.
2. The selling of indulgences, by which a contribution to the church was said to release a soul from purgatory
3. Martin Luther
4. 95 Theses
5. 1517
6. An emphasis on salvation by faith in Christ
7. He translated the Bible into German.
8. Conflicts erupted within countries between Protestants and Catholics, and wars erupted between Catholic monarchies and Protestant monarchies.
9. Henry VIII
10. Lands conquered by the Spanish became Catholic, and lands conquered by the English accepted religious diversity.

Bible Question

The medieval Catholic Church had elaborate cathedrals, a hierarchy of leadership, and great political power.

Lesson 7

1. John Cabot
2. He broke with the Pope and declared himself to be the head of the church in England so he could divorce her.
3. They were daughters by different wives.
4. Roanoke
5. The settlers disappeared for unknown reasons.
6. James I
7. The idea that God places kings on their thrones and thus their decisions cannot be questioned
8. Joint-stock companies financed foreign exploration and trade, the philosophy of mercantilism encouraged government support of business and trade, and the enclosure movement left many rural people in need of a place to live.
9. The idea that government should actively help business, especially in foreign trade and in establishing overseas colonies
10. Spain

Bible Questions

1. Rules about washing hands and dishes, dedicating resources to God rather than helping parents
2. Answers will vary.
3. Answers will vary.

Lesson 8

1. Jamestown, 1607
2. To establish a colony and to spread the gospel
3. A representative assembly for government, and the introduction of black slaves
4. Puritans wanted to reform the Church of England, while Separatists wanted to practice their faith outside of the Church of England.
5. Separatists settled Plymouth, and Puritans settled Massachusetts Bay.
6. Control of the colony was given to members of the company who lived in America, not England.
7. Rhode Island
8. Thomas Hooker
9. Maryland
10. North and South Carolina
11. The Netherlands
12. Quakers
13. The border between Pennsylvania and Maryland
14. To be an economic venture, to be a buffer between the other English colonies and Spanish-controlled Florida, to be a model society, to give debtors in England a new start, and to be a haven for persecuted believers in Europe
15. France

Question on Readings for Lesson 8

1. To earn his wealth from the land, evangelize the heathen, and discover things unknown.
2. To form a "civil body politic" among themselves
3. (1) to be in conformity with the variations in creation, (2) to show the work of God's Spirit as people work together, and (3) that each might need the other
4. To do justly, love mercy, and walk humbly with God; to be knit together as one man; to be kind and sacrificial, etc.
5. Because many people would be watching them to see if the colony succeeded or failed
6. Because the Word of God requires it

Bible Questions

1. To show them kindness and interest, to be good examples of Christians, and also to teach them the gospel

2. Chrstians can be distinct from the world in the way they dress and speak, in showing kindness to others, in what they watch and read, in having more joy and peace. We can hope that demonstrating a better way of life (from the heart, not just for show) will have a positive impact on unbelievers.

Lesson 9

1. To get a new start and to do more with their lives; to have religious freedom; to exercise power over others; slaves were brought against their will.

2. Farming

3. To be an apprentice, then a journeyman, then a craftsman

4. In England, land was scarce and labor was abundant; in America, land was abundant and labor was scarce.

5. Someone who hired himself to work for another person for a set period of time.

6. Women could not vote, preach, hold office, go to college, testify in court or serve on juries, or own property apart from their husbands

7. New England had small farms, more tradesmen, and more involvement in trade, shipping, and fishing. The southern colonies had mostly large plantations and were the most dependent on slavery. The Middle colonies had a mixture of farming, large landowners, and trades; and the middle colonies had larger cities.

8. New England

9. Because people who settled in different regions of America generally came from different regions of the British Isles where the accents were different

10. It was a mixture. Some colonists treated the Indians well and wanted to trade with them and teach them the gospel, while other settlers abused Indians and wanted them out of the way. Some Indian tribes adapted to the settlers, while other tribes fought against the colonists.

Questions on the Poems by Anne Bradstreet

1. Loving and respectful
2. She was thankful and wanted to live well.

Lesson 10

1. Religion was the predominant influence in society. The idea of church and state being separated was foreign to most colonists.

2. The Half-Way Covenant allowed children of non-church members partial status as church members.

3. Calvinism

4. Church of England

5. Apparently from the influence of a slave from the West Indies who practiced witchcraft.

6. Twenty people were executed as witches

7. The Royalists (Cavaliers) and the Puritans (Roundheads)

8. Oliver Cromwell

9. To prevent the Catholic James II and his son from ruling England

10. Parliament asked William and Mary to rule, which meant that the English monarch ruled with the permission of Parliament.

Questions on the *Bay Psalm Book* and the *New England Primer*

1. The *Bay Psalm Book*
2. Lessons from the Bible and moral teachings
3. He decides to follow the devil and live for his pleasures.

Bible Questions

1. Membership in the church is a result of one's being a Christian. Church can become a social activity when people are concerned about being seen at church, how they are dressed, or only concerned about being with their friends.

2. Christians and church leaders should approach such people lovingly (Galatians 6:1) and teach them the truth. If they will not submit to such teaching, the process of Matthew 18:15-20 should be followed.

History Quiz on Unit 2

1. d; 2. a; 3. b; 4. c; 5. d; 6. c; 7. c; 8. d; 9. a; 10. c; 11. b; 12. c; 13. b; 14. d; 15. a; 16. a; 17. a; 18. c; 19. b; 20. b

Unit 3

Lesson 11

1. The Enlightenment was a period of scientific research that established the operation of the universe on the basis of regular scientific laws and that applied reason and natural law to human society.
2. He demonstrated that the earth orbits around the sun.
3. The Catholic church taught that the sun orbits the earth; Copernicus and Galileo showed that this was not the case.
4. That the world operates on the basis of regular scientific laws, such as gravity.
5. They seemed to say that the world operates on the basis of natural law and not on the will of God.
6. He said that people and societies could be changed by education and the application of reason and that political power rested with the people on the basis of social contracts, not with kings.
7. That hereditary monarchy was not a rational form of government
8. Enlightenment thought held that, if the universe operates on the basis of natural law, God is not necessary and miracles are irrational; also, that religion based on faith and tradition is not rational.
9. Man was moved to the center of scientific study and his reason was exalted as ultimate.
10. Studies of the atom and of the universe; the realities of such things as joy, hope, love, and perseverance; and the calamities of war in the twentieth century all challenged a strictly rational approach to life.

Lesson 12

1. Who held power in the colonies and how the colonies were to be governed
2. The king
3. Wealthy colonists who were appointed by the king
4. Free male property owners
5. The British government believed that the assemblies ruled by the permission of the king, while colonists believed that the assemblies ruled by the consent of the governed.
6. The creation of the Dominion of New England to govern the region from London

7. The governor was imprisoned and the colonies resumed their former way of governing.
8. Seditious libel for printing criticism of the royal governor in his newspaper.
9. Zenger was found not guilty, and the verdict encouraged colonial newspapers to publish more criticism of public officials.
10. Encroachment on Indian land, protection for western settlers by colonial governments, and the willingness of colonists to defy governmental authority

Questions on "Sayings from Poor Richard's Almanack"

Answers to all of the questions will vary.

Questions on "Sinners in the Hands of an Angry God"

1. Waters held back for the present, an arrow aimed at your heart, burning fire
2. Insects
3. Various answers possible

Lesson 13

1. The area between the Great Lakes and the Ohio River
2. George Washington
3. Fort Pitt
4. Quebec and Montreal
5. They were forced to leave. Many made their way to New Orleans (and came to be called Cajuns).
6. Spain
7. Great Britain
8. By raising taxes on the colonies
9. France helped the United States in the Revolutionary War against England.
10. To create a central government for the American colonies, so that they might act in a unified fashion if the need arose.

Questions on the Albany Plan of Union

1. The President-General
2. By the king
3. By the colonial legislatures
4. At least once a year
5. The king

Lesson 14

1. Same language and culture, same legal system, same trades and social classes; belief in representative government and individual rights; upper class American sons often educated in England; colonists saw selves as subjects of the crown
2. No royalty in America; Americans envisioned new possibilities for their lives; the frontier experience, including log cabins and Indian attacks.
3. The standing army in the colonies, with troops quartered in private homes.
4. Royal control over laws passed by colonial assemblies, writs of assistance, colonies not allowed to print money, new taxes passed.
5. The king forbade any settlement by English subjects west of the crest of the Appalachian Mountains.
6. Many colonists wanted to settle the western region. They thought that they had fought the French and Indian War to be able to do so, but now it was forbidden.
7. They believed that such taxes were wrong and could not be enacted by Parliament.
8. A confrontation between Boston citizens and British soldiers. British soldiers fired into the crowd and killed several colonists.
9. Because it allowed the East India Company to dump cheap tea onto the colonial market, thus making the colonies dependent on the British company for tea.
10. The Coercive or Intolerable Acts.

Questions on Letter 2 from "Letters From a Farmer in Pennsylvania"

1. To regulate the trade of Britain and the colonies
2. They were solely for the purpose of raising revenue.
3. They limited the freedom of the colonies to conduct business as they desired and made the colonies dependent on products from Britain for which they had to pay taxes
4. Slaves

Bible Question

They had to return to following God's Law and they had to restore the observance of the Feast of Booths.

Lesson 15

1. A general decline. Factors included worldliness, church becoming a social institution, a lack of religious interest on the western frontier, and the rise of Enlightenment and Deist thinking.
2. George Whitefield, John Wesley
3. A revival movement in the American colonies during the mid-1700s
4. Jonathan Edwards
5. They felt threatened when evangelists described churches as dead and preachers as unconverted.
6. Whether to endorse the revival or not.
7. The formation of Unitarian and Universalist churches.
8. Colleges; Princeton, Columbia, Brown, Rutgers, and Dartmouth
9. Revivalist preaching, multifaceted Christianity, individual decisions, hope for the millennium.
10. The need for spiritual revival

History Question

The family studies show that how we live can affect our family for generations, both for good and for ill.

English Questions

1. Sins of the community and others: judgmentalism, hypocrisy; Dimmesdale was hypocritical and did not confess his sin; Chillingsworth was cruel.
2. Symbolism of Hester's home: Hester's life was on the border between light and darkness. She had committed a great sin, but she was trying to do what was right thereafter.
3. Comparison to John 8:1-11: In each case, a woman was caught in adultery and the community leaders condemned her. In John, Jesus pointed out the leaders' sin and gave the woman hope and instruction.

Bible Questions

1. Not being hypocritical: be honest with yourself; accept instruction and correction from others about how you act; honestly study the Bible and let its message change you.
2. How respond to someone: show love toward that person, help her see her wrong, kindly encourage her repentance, help her start over
3. How the story could have been different: Hester and her child could have made positive

contributions to the community, the community leaders could have grown and been different, Dimmesdale's life might have been spared.

4. Risk by that leader: A leader who showed a Christ-like attitude might have been condemned by others.

5. "Your sin will find you out": The sins of the main characters were revealed and they had to suffer the consequences for them.

Questions on *The Scarlet Letter*

1. A dark, sad, and musty tone
2. Hawthorne tells how he got the idea for the story.
3. They were hateful and unforgiving toward her.
4. Pearl was strong-willed. Some thought that she was a devil-child as retribution for the sin which conceived her.
5. To find out the secrets of Arthur Dimmesdale's life and to seek revenge for what he had done with Hester.
6. Dimmesdale
7. They believed that he could do no wrong. They thought he was strong but in fact he was weak.
8. He carved an A on his chest and stood on the scaffold at night.
9. They planned to run away to Europe together.
10. He died before he was able to leave the community.
11. He died within a year of Dimmesdale's death and left an inheritance for Pearl.
12. She moved to Europe and was not directly heard from again.
13. She left for many years; but later she returned to the community, helped many people, and died there.
14. It shows the failings of a community that was supposedly build on faith in Christ
15. Their focus was on Hester's sin. One key factor might have been that men were leaders of the community.
16. Hester was able to admit her responsibility for her sin and move on in her life. Dimmesdale kept his sin hidden and it eventually destroyed him.
17. She took the responsibility for rearing Pearl; she helped others; she did not strike back when others reviled her.
18. Possible reasons: She loved Arthur and wanted to be near him; life outside of the community would have been even more difficult; other answers possible

History Quiz on Unit 3

1. a; 2. b; 3. d; 4. c; 5. b; 6. a; 7. c; 8. b; 9. a; 10. d

Unit 4

Lesson 16

1. He declared the colonies to be in a state of rebellion.
2. Patrick Henry
3. To arrest Sam Adams and John Hancock and to seize a stockpile of patriot weapons
4. They tried to warn Adams, Hancock, and militiamen in Lexington and Concord.
5. The British troops were defeated and retreated back into Boston.
6. George Washington
7. The British (though at a high cost)
8. The Olive Branch Petition and the Declaration of the Causes and Necessity of Taking Up Arms
9. To show a conciliatory attitude toward King George III
10. World opinion (to justify armed resistance to the British king and armed forces)

Questions on "Give Me Liberty or Give Me Death!"

1. Freedom or slavery
2. The lamp of experience
3. Fight
4. He said that God would raise up friends to fight for them.
5. Chains and slavery

Questions on "Paul Revere's Ride" and "Concord Hymn"

1. One (lamp) if by land and two if by sea
2. The Old North Church in Boston
3. "To every Middlesex village and farm"
4. Dramatic unfolding of events, relief at its conclusion
5. They fired the shot heard round the world.
6. A monument was being erected.
7. Emerson wrote from the perspective of history. He wanted future generations to remember what was done at the bridge. He wrote with a settled sense of acceptance of what had been done there.

Lesson 17

1. Thomas Paine
2. Thomas Jefferson
3. Congress adopted Lee's resolution that the colonies were free and independent states.
4. Congress adopted the Declaration of Independence.
5. Enlightenment thinking
6. To tell the world the United States' reasons for declaring their independence from Great Britain
7. The king
8. The Olive Branch Petition sought reconciliation with the king, while the Declaration of Independence stated the colonies' break with the king.
9. One-third wanted to remain with Britain, one-third wanted independence, and one-third was unsure and waiting to be convinced.
10. Tories and Whigs

Questions on "Common Sense"

1. A necessary evil
2. The heathens
3. Because of a national delusion
4. April 19 (1775)—the skirmishes at Lexington and Concord
5. None

Questions on the Declaration of Independence

1. It says that the step is necessary.
2. All men are created equal; all are endowed by God with certain inalienable rights; that among these are life, liberty, and the pursuit of happiness; that governments are formed by the consent of the governed to secure these rights; that when a form of government becomes destructive of these ends, it is the right of the people to alter or abolish it and institute a new form of government to secure these rights.
3. A reference to the laws of Nature and of Nature's God; the fact that God created man, that He created them equal, and that He gives them inalienable rights; an appeal to the Supreme Judge of the world for the correctness of this step; a firm reliance on the protection of Divine Providence.
4. Their lives, their fortunes, and their sacred honor
5. Thirteen

Questions on the Poems by Phillis Wheatley

1. She was able to learn the gospel and to be rescued from darkness.
2. Near
3. The knowledge of the universe and of Christ
4. To shun evil

Lesson 18

1. Britain was the most industrialized nation in the world; it was a wealthy country; it had a strong navy and a experienced, victorious army; during the war it won many battles and held several major cities
2. Smaller population, no standing army, small navy, untrained militia, not a strong central government, some weak state governments, no strong national currency, soldiers poorly paid and equipped
3. To control the major cities and divide New England from the rest of the colonies
4. Washington's army camped there in difficult conditions during the severe winter of 1777-1778.
5. a. British; b. Americans; c. Americans; d. British; e. Americans
6. The surrender of Burgoyne's British forces at Saratoga. It was a victory for the United States and it brought France into the war on the side of the U.S.
7. The Battle of King's Mountain
8. October 19, 1781
9. Poor military leaders, fighting far from home, tenuous supply lines, the failure of British diplomacy with the American colonies
10. Washington's leadership, American soldiers fought better, they were on their home soil, the developing consciousness of being Americans, assistance from France.

Questions on "The Crisis"

1. Its dearness, the price we have to pay for it
2. He thought God would not abandon a people to military conquest who had tried so hard to avoid conflict.
3. As a participant in the army

Lesson 19

1. Families suffered the absence and loss of many husbands, fathers, and sons; property

was destroyed in battle and by the movement of armies.

2. The U.S. population was divided, with many colonists remaining loyal to Britain and eventually leaving the United States.

3. Colonial government office-holders, Anglican clergy, some businessmen, and many small farmers

4. Government and society were relatively stable, but the economy was severely disrupted.

5. It was encouraged by the American victory.

6. Daniel Boone

7. More opportunity for land ownership, the building of wealth, and the need for skilled craftsmen; work opportunities beyond being servants and indentured servants.

8. Bills of rights, greater political liberties, expanded right to vote

9. The Articles of Confederation

10. Disposition of western lands

Questions on the Articles of Confederation

1. A firm league of friendship
2. Between two and seven
3. By states, with each state having one vote
4. Nine
5. The states

Lesson 20

1. God
2. As the work of God
3. It was a turn of events from the Lord.
4. Because Israel had been unfaithful to the Lord
5. His shepherd and His anointed
6. No, He creates democracies also.
7. By using principles we find in the Bible
8. Either He is or He isn't.
9. We should realize that God is still in charge.
10. God

History Quiz on Unit 4

1. b; 2. b; 3. c; 4. b; 5. d; 6. b; 7. b; 8. a; 9. a; 10. a; 11. c; 12. c; 13. a; 14. c; 15. d; 16. d; 17. a; 18. b; 19. a; 20. d

Unit 5

Lesson 21

1. Economic stability, economic crises in the states, frontier Indian attacks, foreign relations

2. The organization of territories and how territories could become states

3. 1787

4. George Washington

5. James Madison

6. How the states would be represented in Congress

7. Electors would be chosen in every state who would vote for president

8. Three-fifths of the slaves would be counted for taxation and representation

9. Essays published in support of ratification of the Constitution

10. Antifederalists

Questions on "The Federalist Number 10"

1. Factions
2. Destroying liberty and giving everyone the same opinions
3. The various and unequal distribution of property
4. Controlling their effects
5. A larger republic

Bible Questions

1. By walking in the law of the Lord
2. By keeping it according to God's Word
3. So that he might not sin against God
4. He rejoices in it; it is his delight.
5. God's Word

Lesson 22

1. A careful series of balances and compromises, expectation that the new government would be driven by Congress, fear of democracy

2. Delegated or enumerated powers, separation of powers, checks and balances

3. Senate and House of Representatives

4. Every two years

5. To initiate revenue bills, and to initiate the impeachment process

6. Six years

7. One-third

8. To ratify treaties, to approve presidential nominations, to try impeachment cases

9. When a bill is introduced, it is assigned to a committee of that body (either the House or the Senate). If the committee considers it and votes it out, the entire body can consider it and vote on

it. If it passes, it is sent to the other house for the same process. If the two versions are different, a compromise committee writes a single version. When both houses pass the identical bill, it is sent to the president. The president can either sign it (and it becomes law), veto it and return it to Congress (which must pass it with a two-thirds majority in both houses), or not sign it in a pocket veto (the bill still becomes law after ten days if Congress is still in session).

10. See the previous answer

Bible Question

More valuable than thousands of gold and silver pieces

Lesson 23

1. Four years
2. Two
3. Electors, or the electoral college
4. 538 (one for each senator and congressman plus three for the District of Columbia)
5. He is commander in chief.
6. He oversees the executive branch in carrying out the laws.
7. He is head of state, negotiates treaties, and receives foreign heads of state.
8. Accusation
9. District, appeals, supreme
10. Each state is to give full faith and credit to the laws and actions of every other state.

Bible Questions
1. All day
2. It is a lamp to his feet and a light to his path.

Lesson 24

1. Two-thirds of both houses of Congress and three-fourths of the states
2. Freedom of religion, freedom of speech, freedom of the press, the right to petition the government
3. The right to keep and bear arms
4. Rights of the accused
5. All powers not expressly delegated to Congress nor denied to the states are reserved to the states and people
6. A Federal income tax
7. Give women the right to vote
8. The poll tax

9. Presidential succession
10. Give eighteen-year-olds the right to vote

Bible Questions

1. Law, commandments, testimonies, ways, precepts, statutes, ordinances.
2. Answers will vary, but we hope they will be positive!
3. Answers will vary.
4. Have a regular time to study; read through the Bible regularly; study books of the Bible individually and more intensely; pray to put into practice what you read; be accountable to someone for your actions.
5. Divisions over interpretations of certain passages; doctrines that emerge from one person's private interpretation; other answers possible

Lesson 25

1. The Bible
2. Final, inspired, infallible, not to be added to or taken from
3. Determining what a text says and determining what a text means
4. Everyone
5. The way it was written
6. Taking a verse out of context to defend an already-established belief or practice
7. Other passages of Scripture
8. God
9. Jesus
10. Scripture interprets us.

History Quiz on Unit 5

1. B; 2. G; 3. I; 4. F; 5. C; 6. A; 7. E; 8. D; 9. J; 10. H; 11. X; 12. P; 13. S; 14. M; 15. T; 16. K; 17. U; 18. Y; 19. W; 20. V; 21. N; 22. L; 23. R; 24. Q; 25. O

History Test on Units 1-5

1. Condemned to repeat it
2. Possible answers: expansion, power and control, mixture of good and evil, ethnocentrism, interwoven nature of events (the fabric of history)
3. The Roman Catholic Church
4. Renaissance
5. Aztec
6. He thought the distance was much less than it is, and he did not count on a continental land mass being in the way.

7. Spain

8. Ethnocentrism

9. Italian explorer Amerigo Vespucci

10. St. Augustine

11. Henry VIII

12. John Cabot

13. Roanoke

14. The idea that kings are placed on their thrones by God and therefore cannot be questioned

15. The Spanish Armada

16. Jamestown, 1607

17. Separatists (or Pilgrims)

18. Puritans

19. Maryland

20. Mayflower Compact

21. A city on a hill

22. People who sold themselves into service to another for a period of time, after which they were free

23. They came to the throne at the request and with the permission of Parliament

24. The economic and political philosophy that said government should actively assist business, especially in trade and planting colonies

25. The governor

26. George Washington

27. Louisiana

28. Great Britain

29. A protest against lower tea prices

30. Patrick Henry

31. Yes

32. Saratoga

33. Cornwallis

34. Daniel Boone

35. Articles of Confederation

36. 1787

37. How the states would be represented in Congress

38. How slaves were to be counted for taxation and to determine representation in Congress

39. Checks and balances

40. Congress

41. Two years

42. Six years

43. Four years

44. The vice president of the United States

45. One-third

46. Veto

47. Committees

48. District, Appeals, Supreme

49. The Bill of Rights

50. The 1st Amendment

English Test on Units 1-5

1. Anne Bradstreet

2. *Bay Psalm Book*

3. *New England Primer*

4. Journals

5. Michael Wigglesworth

6. *Poor Richard's Almanack*

7. Adultery or adulteress

8. The thought he was strong and upright, but in fact he was weak and was an adulterer also.

9. Sin that is kept hidden eats away and destroys, but sin that is dealt with openly can be overcome.

10. Henry Wadsworth Longfellow

11. Drama, excitement, anticipation

12. Ralph Waldo Emerson

13. The dedication of a monument at the bridge where fighting took place in 1775

14. Thomas Paine

15. She was able to learn the gospel.

16. *The Federalist* or *The Federalist Papers*

17. *The Federalist Number 10*

18. "The Crisis"

19. *Poor Richard's Almanack*

20. *The Scarlet Letter*

Bible Test on Units 1-5

1. To help the people remember their history

2. How a person sees and understands the world in which he or she lives

3. Choose from: the belief that God made the world, that God made man in His image as a special creation, that God guides the world, that all is to be for God's glory, that He gave absolute standards of right and wrong, that the world is heading for judgment

4. Indulgences

5. Martin Luther

6. 95 Theses

7. Protestant Reformation

8. Offer some benefits of church membership to the children of the unconverted

9. Protestant

10. Roger Williams

11. Religious toleration

12. It pushed God to the sidelines by saying that the world operates by fixed natural laws; it also challenged religious tradition and even religious faith.

13. A period of spiritual revival in the American colonies

14. The middle of the 1700s
15. Jonathan Edwards
16. God is angry with man for his sins and barely holds back His wrath against man. People need to repent and come to God or face this wrath.
17. Some preachers condemned churches as spiritually dead and ministers as unconverted.
18. Colleges
19. That He rules and that He guides what happens
20. The Bible
21. Determining what a text says, and determining what a text means
22. The rest of Scripture
23. Jesus
24. Taking a verse out of context to support an already existing belief or practice
25. God's Word

Unit 6

Lesson 26

1. George Washington, John Adams
2. New York City
3. 1789
4. State—Thomas Jefferson; Treasury—Alexander Hamilton; War—Henry Knox
5. Cabinet
6. That the Federal government assume the debts under the Confederation and of the states
7. The establishment of a national bank
8. Assistance for manufacturers, specifically the enactment of protective tariffs
9. Pennsylvania; opposition to a Federal tax on whiskey
10. Ohio; it helped western settlement

Questions on George Washington's First Inaugural Address and his Thanksgiving Proclamation

1. He was pulled by the desire to serve his country, but he was awed at the responsibility he was to fulfill.
2. Supplications to God
3. He saw God's hand in every step of the formation of the new nation.
4. A nation that disregards the eternal rules of order and right
5. He did not want to be paid for serving as President.
6. "To acknowledge the providence of Almighty

God, to obey his will, to be grateful for his benefits, and humbly to implore his protection and favor."
7. For God's protection before they became a nation, for His guidance during the war, for their tranquility and plenty since the war, for the peaceful establishment of government, and for the many favors He had bestowed
8. For pardon for their national transgressions, help in performing their duties well, to render the national government a blessing, to protect sovereigns and nations, and to grant prosperity

Bible Questions

1. Matthew 22:15-22—Jesus wanted His followers to focus on the more important issue, which was submission to God. Paying taxes to Caesar did not prevent that.
2. Romans 13:1-7—Paul did not want the Christian movement to get bogged down in a political battle over secular government. He saw even pagan government as a help to the furthering of the gospel.

Lesson 27

1. How to respond to the French Revolution
2. The U.S. gave diplomatic recognition to the new French government.
3. He issued a proclamation of neutrality.
4. He tried to outfit French ships and he encouraged attacks on Spanish-held territory in the western hemisphere.
5. Stopping and seizing ships bound for enemy ports and impressment of those they claimed were British deserters.
6. An agreement with Great Britain, but it did not resolve important issues favorably in the opinion of many Americans.
7. It settled Spanish claims in North America outside of Florida and guaranteed American access to New Orleans.
8. A strong central government, the development of industry, and leadership by the elite
9. A weak central government with strong state governments, an agriculture-based economy, and a trust of the average citizen
10. The formation of political parties

Questions on George Washington's Farewell Address

1. Division, suspicion, the desire for revenge, despotism of one party over the other
2. Religion and morality
3. The general diffusion of knowledge
4. Positive trade relations but no standing political alliances
5. Neutrality

Questions on "The Legend of Rip Van Winkle"

1. A work of fiction shorter than a novel, with fewer characters and usually only one plot line
2. He was kind, easygoing, and lazy. She was harsh and suspicious.
3. Odd-looking people playing ninepins
4. His house was deserted, the inn was gone, the picture of King George III had been replaced by one of George Washington.
5. Just like his father
6. It explained thunder in the mountains and gave henpecked husbands a way to express their desire to be free of domestic unhappiness.
7. It describes and depends on the geographic layout of the region; it describes local attitudes and customs; it uses Dutch names common in the area; it is dependent on the time frame in which it is set.

Bible Questions

1. By understanding the teachings and patterns in Scripture and by knowing what is really at stake in the issue, namely whether obeying the government in this issue is really disobeying God
2. A public official must serve and represent people with many different beliefs. He wants to be fair to all while maintaining his own principles. He might be tempted to downplay his faith in order to appeal to a broader segment of the population.

Lesson 28

1. Federalist: John Adams and Thomas Pinckney; Republican: Thomas Jefferson and Aaron Burr
2. John Adams was elected President, and Thomas Jefferson was elected Vice President.
3. French representatives asked the Americans for a bribe, a large loan, and an apology just to begin negotiations.

4. Adams referred to the French representatives as X, Y, and Z; so it came to be known as the XYZ Affair.
5. He resisted calls for war with France and negotiated a new agreement with that country.
6. To limit foreign influence and to weaken the Republicans, who were widely supported by new immigrants
7. Naturalization Act: increased the time required for aliens to become citizens; Alien and Alien Enemy Acts: gave the president greater rights to imprison or deport those he saw as dangerous to the country; Sedition Act: outlawed false, scandalous, and malicious attacks on the government
8. To promote one political party over another
9. The Virginia and Kentucky Resolutions, which raised serious questions about the laws
10. Ten people (all Republicans) were prosecuted under the Sedition Act, and these became martyrs for the Republican cause. The laws diminished respect for the Federalists in the minds of many Americans.

Questions on the Virginia and Kentucky Resolutions

1. The states' loyalty to the country and the Constitution
2. Concerns about the Federal government overstepping its authority
3. The belief that the Alien and Sedition Laws were unconstitutional
4. To stand together in opposing a loss of their rights and freedoms at the expense of the national government
5. Nullification (refusing to enforce unconstitutional laws)

Bible Questions

1. Various answers possible, including liberal theology, denial of God and of the inspiration and authority of Scripture; Eastern religions, New Age ideas, secular philosophy.
2. The gospel tells those who do not have much in this life that they are valuable and worthwhile. Those who are wealthy and powerful in this life are challenged to give up what they have.

Lesson 29

1. Federalist: John Adams and Charles Pinckney; Republicans: Thomas Jefferson and Aaron Burr

2. Thomas Jefferson
3. Hateful, vicious, and mean-spirited
4. John Adams
5. An attempt by the lame-duck Federalist Congress to control the Federal judiciary
6. John Marshall
7. 3.9 million
8. Sixteen
9. Vermont, Kentucky, Tennessee, Ohio
10. 5.3 million

Questions on "A Man Worth Knowing"

1. Nominating George Washington to command the Continental Army, encouraging Thomas Jefferson to write the Declaration of Independence, and nominating John Marshall as Chief Justice
2. To help get French aid for the American cause
3. The Massachusetts state constitution
4. He arranged for the Netherlands to give loans to the U.S.
5. Joyful and optimistic

Bible Questions

1. Philippians 2:14-16. Christians are bombarded with ungodly messages and influenced by friends and prominent people to abandon their faith and follow the world.
2. It helps in that people are familiar with the gospel, but it hurts in that many people think they are just fine with God just by being in that society.

Lesson 30

1. The identity of the church, the relationship between the church and government, and the nature of an individual's walk with God
2. Toleration of religious diversity
3. The idea of a community or a nation being founded for a religious purpose
4. Religiously active, individual freedom, diversity of distinctive American religious groups
5. Most had a strong faith in God, although we might not agree with all of their theology today.
6. John Jay
7. Rationalistic belief (such as Deism)
8. A decline in church membership took place during this time.
9. Civil religion
10. The mottoes "In God We Trust" and "One Nation Under God," official statements that men-

tion God, recognition of God in official actions, tax exemptions for churches without established churches, maintaining a balance between freedom of religion and freedom from religion, recognition of God without an established religion

Questions on the Virginia Statute for Religious Freedom

1. Because God created the mind free but attempts to confine it in religious matters have resulted in evils
2. Makes hypocrites of people who profess the accepted faith but do not practice it
3. Civil rights have no dependence on our religious opinions
4. No one will be forced to support any religious leader, church or ministry; and no one will suffer because of his beliefs.
5. That any attempt to repeal or change the statute will be a violation of natural law

History Quiz on Unit 6

1. N; 2. H; 3. O; 4. E; 5. F; 6. A; 7. M; 8. D; 9. L; 10. C; 11. J; 12. K; 13. G; 14. I; 15. B

Unit 7

Lesson 31

1. Washington, Adams, Jefferson
2. Alexander Hamilton
3. Jefferson and Burr tied in the electoral college. The House of Representatives chose Jefferson.
4. The Revolution of 1800
5. The Louisiana Purchase
6. Meriwether Lewis and William Clark
7. Missouri River
8. Sacajawea
9. The importation of slaves
10. Jefferson

Questions on Thomas Jefferson's First Inaugural Address

1. The other men holding office on whom he could rely
2. Republicans, Federalists
3. "Can he, then, be trusted with the government of others?"
4. George Washington
5. "That infinite power which rules the destinies of the universe"

Questions on "I Love Thy Kingdom, Lord"

1. The house of Thine abode; the church
2. Her sweet communion, solemn vows, and her hymns of love and praise
3. Jesus'

Lesson 32

1. John Marshall
2. Virginia
3. He was a strong supporter of the Constitution and of a strong national government.
4. Secretary of State James Madison refused to give William Marbury his commission that President Adams had signed, and Marbury sued for it in the Supreme Court according to the Judiciary Act of 1801.
5. Marshall said that Marbury was entitled to it.
6. It was unconstitutional since it gave the Supreme Court original jurisdiction in an area which the Constitution did not give it.
7. It said that the Court had the power to determine what the law is and to decide if a law is void because it violates the Constitution.
8. It upheld the National Bank, and thus the "necessary and proper" clause; and it denied that a state could control or regulate an activity of the Federal government.
9. The law itself
10. When judges inject their own opinions into interpreting the law

Questions on *Marbury v. Madison*

1. The Constitution is supreme.
2. "To say what the law is."
3. The courts
4. Void

Bible Questions

For each passage: the period during which it took place, what the religious error was, and who led the call for restoration.

Exodus 32—during the exodus from Egypt; the worship of the golden calf; Moses
Judges 2:11-23—during the period of the judges; the worship of Baal and other pagan deities; the judges
2 Kings 12—In Judah during the divided kingdom; the need to repair the temple and restore the proper worship practices; King Jehoash (or Joash)

Lesson 33

1. Great Britain and France
2. The Embargo Act, which primarily hurt the U.S.
3. The West
4. Just before Congress declared war, the British government had decided to ease interference with American trade and appeared ready to negotiate on other matters.
5. New England
6. Washington, D.C.
7. Baltimore
8. Andrew Jackson
9. New Orleans. It was fought after the peace treaty had been signed.
10. The U.S. held the British at bay and also had a burst of optimism and self-confidence.

Questions on the Letters from John Adams and Thomas Jefferson

1. Justice for everyone and the golden rule
2. Virtue and talents
3. Wealth and birth
4. The real good and wise
5. Explained themselves to each other

Questions on "The Star-Spangled Banner"

1. After a British bombardment of Ft. McHenry in 1814
2. The star-spangled banner
3. "The Pow'r that hath made and preserved us a nation"
4. "In God is our trust"
5. The land of the free and the home of the brave

Bible Questions

For each passage: the period during which it took place, what the religious error was, and who led the call for restoration.

2 Kings 18:1-6—Late kingdom of Judah, worship of pagan idols; Hezekiah
2 Kings 22:1-23:25—Late kingdom of Judah; failure to know or follow the Law; Josiah
Ezra 3:1-13, 6:13-22, chapters 9 and 10—return from exile; not worshiping at the temple accord-

ing to the Law and marrying people of the land; Ezra

Lesson 34

1. It had expanded from 13 states along the east coast to cover two-thirds of the continent.
2. Virginia
3. The Era of Good Feelings
4. Appropriate: Only one major political party, a general feeling of growth and goodwill across the country; inappropriate: political divisions still existed, the economy was weak, the issue of slavery was starting to divide the country.
5. Debt from the War of 1812, the closing of the first Bank of the U.S. in 1811, the unregulated activity of state banks, the inability of American agriculture to meet the opportunities of foreign trade
6. A protective tariff, the creation of the Second Bank of the United States, a system of internal transportation improvements
7. The desire to settle new land, cheaper land prices, immigration
8. Cumberland, Maryland to Vandalia, Illinois
9. Erie Canal
10. The steamboat

Questions on "Thanatopsis" and "To a Waterfowl"

1. Nature
2. Go out and listen to Nature's teachings
3. With kings, the wise, the good—all of mankind
4. The tomb of man
5. Share thy destiny
6. "To that mysterious realm" of death
7. Sustained and soothed by an unfaltering trust, lie down to pleasant dreams
8. Where are you going?
9. God
10. God will guide him aright also.

Bible Questions

For each passage: the period during which it took place, what the religious error was, and who led the call for restoration.

Matthew 21:12-13—the ministry of Jesus; buying and selling in the temple; Jesus
Hebrews 10:32-36—during persecution in the church; a lack of faith; the author of Hebrews

Revelation 2:1-7—Ephesus; they had grown weary and left their first love; Jesus

Lesson 35

1. The Revolutionary War and the break from English-based churches, Enlightenment and Deistic thinking, the movement west to settle new lands and acquire wealth, the rough lifestyle on the frontier
2. Just north of Lexington, Kentucky
3. Between 10,000 and 30,000.
4. The "exercises" (uncontrolled physical reactions such as falling, jerking, dancing, barking, and laughing)
5. Congregations became more numerous and larger, they had more influence in communities; people began to see faith as a matter of personal decision, not something predestined
6. That anyone could understand the Bible by studying it rationally with common sense
7. That they should live the way church members did, and that they did not need extensive specialized training.
8. Many people wanted to leave denominational groupings and simply follow the New Testament
9. The Cumberland Presbyterian Church and the Disciples (Christian Church/Churches of Christ)
10. The millennium

Questions on "The Last Will and Testament of the Springfield Presbytery"

1. The Bible
2. God
3. For each to hire its own
4. The Bible
5. He might be cast into hell.

Questions on *Narrative of the Life of David Crockett*

All of these questions have subjective or various possible answers.

History Quiz on Unit 7

1. Thomas Jefferson
2. Meriwether Lewis, William Clark
3. Sacajawea
4. Alexander Hamilton
5. Aaron Burr

6. John Marshall
7. James Madison
8. James Monroe
9. Andrew Jackson
10. Henry Clay
11. Robert Fulton
12. Jefferson's First Inaugural Address
13. *Marbury v. Madison* Supreme Court decision
14. Letter from Thomas Jefferson to John Adams
15. The Last Will and Testament of the Springfield Presbytery

Unit 8

Lesson 36

1. All of them
2. The seven northernmost ones
3. Admitted a slave state and a free state at the same time
4. Sectionalism
5. New England favored protective tariffs while the South opposed them.
6. Slaves states wanted slavery to be extended into the territories while free states opposed it.
7. It raised the issue of slavery in the Louisiana Territory, and a proposal was made in Congress for the gradual abolition of slavery in Missouri.
8. Henry Clay
9. In the Louisiana Territory north of the 36°30' latitude line, except for Missouri itself
10. Yes, slavery was allowed in Missouri.

Bible Question

1 John 2:23—Perhaps they think that Christianity is old-fashioned and that the modern age should have more modern answers; perhaps they have seen failings in how Christianity has been practiced and feel a need to look elsewhere; perhaps they pridefully want to be "in the know" as part of a new thought world.

Lesson 37

1. Washington, Adams, Jefferson, Madison, Monroe
2. Caution and neutrality
3. Being able to trade with other countries
4. De-militarizing the Great Lakes, affirming fishing rights, establishing the U.S.-Canadian border, agreeing to joint occupation of the Oregon Territory

5. Spain ceded Florida to the United States, and the western border of the Louisiana Territory was established.
6. They discussed whether European armies should intervene in the popular revolutions of other countries.
7. Trade relations and the possibility of acquiring other territories
8. European nations should not consider any part of the western hemisphere for future colonization, and any attempt to do so would be seen as a threat to the United States; the United States said it would not interfere with European colonies in the western hemisphere nor in European wars.
9. The British navy
10. Soviet involvement in the Communist revolution in Cuba

Questions on the Monroe Doctrine

1. Russia
2. It had never taken any part.
3. The U.S. had not interfered and would not interfere.
4. The manifestation of an unfriendly disposition toward the United States
5. Spain and Portugal

Bible Question

2 Corinthians 10:12—It is attractive because it is comfortable and can change as we change. If man is our standard, we will always be right! It is dangerous, however, because one person cannot see clearly enough to set everyone's standard; standards of society change; and we would wind up saying that some things are right which are actually wrong and vice versa.

Lesson 38

1. Ambassador to the Netherlands and to Russia; Secretary of State
2. The Monroe Doctrine
3. Secretary of State
4. Jackson, Adams, Clay, Crawford
5. Jackson
6. The House of Representatives selected Adams.
7. Jackson had gotten the most votes but he was not chosen; and he suspected a "corrupt bargain" between Clay and Adams for Adams to be elected President and Clay to be appointed Secretary of State.

8. The Tariff of 1828 (the "Tariff of Abominations")

9. Congressman from Massachusetts

10. He opposed the expansion of slavery and promoted the Smithsonian Institution.

Bible Question

Matthew 24:36—We find it difficult to trust something that we do not know or do not have a grasp of. We like to have inside information. Sometimes a person who tries to set the date wants to sell something or to control other people.

Lesson 39

1. His capture by the British and his abuse at the hands of a British officer.

2. He was named public prosecutor for the Western District of North Carolina (the area that became Tennessee).

3. Lewis Robards

4. Andrew and Rachel accidentally got married while Rachel was still married to Robards.

5. He served in the state constitutional convention and was a congressman and senator from the state and a superior court judge and major general of the state militia.

6. The victory over the British that he led in the Battle of New Orleans

7. He thought that many of its leaders were corrupt and were using their positions for personal gain.

8. Henry Clay

9. Andrew Jackson and John C. Calhoun

10. Rachel Jackson died.

Bible Question

Hebrews 13:9—Some people find it hard to accept that Christ is the single answer. Certain aspects of other systems are attractive to some people. We can avoid being enticed by knowing the Bible well and grounding our beliefs firmly in God and His Word.

Lesson 40

1. That He is one and not three Persons

2. That all will be saved

3. Charles G. Finney

4. The Over-Soul

5. Joseph Smith

6. They believe that God is married and that human marriages can be eternal. They also accepted polygamy for many years.

7. Brigham Young

8. The second coming of Christ

9. Utopian

10. Shakertown, (New) Harmony, Oneida, Brook Farm

Questions on *Narrative of the Life of Frederick Douglass*

1. A slave woman and a white man, perhaps his master.

2. He saw it as harsh, demeaning, and inhumane. He recognized that it demeaned slaveowners as well as slaves.

3. Whites generally thought it was a waste of time and dangerous.

4. Shipbuilding

5. He found them generally to be the harshest owners.

6. He believed in and respected the Christianity of the Bible, but he had no respect for the Christianity practiced in the United States because it was hypocritical and supported the harsh and violent institution of slavery.

7. He is determined to portray the harsh realities of slavery, and he conveys his own determination not to bow to the institution.

Bible Questions

1. Because people are sinful and cannot create a perfect community.

2. They were more concerned about giving than about getting. They did not have man's rules imposed on them.

History Quiz on Unit 8

All of the statements are false.

Unit 9

Lesson 41

1. It reflected the greater power of the average American; it showed the growing political power of the West.

2. He thought that those who filled such jobs should be rotated out on a regular basis; he also believed that the winning political party should

be able to fill government positions with its supporters.

3. South Carolina

4. That a state had the right to nullify or refuse to enforce a Federal law it believed was unconstitutional

5. He believed it was unconstitutional; he believed it had not provided a sound and uniform national currency; he believed the bank had gotten involved in politics; he was leery of paper money.

6. "Pet banks"

7. They probably contributed to an economic downturn, culminating in the Panic of 1837.

8. The policy of the Federal government to force Indian tribes to give up their land within states in exchange for other land west of the Mississippi.

9. The Cherokee Trail of Tears

10. Anti-Mason party

Questions on Daniel Webster's Second Reply to Robert Hayne

1. Their unity in the Revolution

2. That states had the right to nullify a Federal law

3. Rope of sand

4. From the people (not the states)

5. Liberty and union

Questions on "The Growth of American Literature"

1. D; 2. H; 3. G; 4. A; 5. F; 6. I; 7. B; 8. J; 9. C; 10. E

Bible Questions

1. Thankful for America, its past, its natural beauty, the blessings it offers; offers a prayer to God to protect the country.

2. The song combines faith in God with patriotic feeling.

Lesson 42

1. Martin Van Buren

2. Secretary of State, Vice President

3. Whig

4. By fielding several regional candidates to run against Van Buren

5. The Panic of 1837

6. Independent treasury

7. Whig: William Henry Harrison; Democrat:

Martin Van Buren

8. Harrison died a month after taking office.

9. Not well. The Whigs cast him out of the party.

10. Westward expansion

Questions on *Democracy in America*

1. Religious mores

2. Religion

3. To raise the souls of their fellow citizens and turn their attention toward heaven

4. They were all-consuming for candidates and the people

5. The presence of black slaves in the country

Questions on Poetry

1. Stanza

2. Meter

3. Iambic pentameter

4. Alliteration

5. Onomatopoeia

Questions on "Old Ironsides"

1. The USS *Constitution* was in danger of being scrapped.

2. Sarcastic, but also sad that the ship was being condemned.

Question on "Lord of All Being, Throned Afar"

Attributes of God: Creator of the universe; Giver of life, hope, truth, and love

Lesson 43

1. The idea that it was clear (manifest) that America's God-given destiny was to own and govern the land that stretched from the east coast of the U.S. to the west coast

2. Oregon Trail

3. Great Britain and the United States

4. Part of Mexico

5. Moses Austin

6. Stephen Austin

7. Settlers from the U.S. in the province of Texas. They declared their independence in 1836.

8. The Alamo

9. San Jacinto

10. The new Mexican government refused to recognize Texas independence.

Questions on "The Arrow and the Song" and "I Hear America Singing"

1. In an oak tree
2. In the heart of a friend
3. What you do influences others, and you never know where that influence might wind up.
4. Because many Americans sing while doing their work and at play
5. Each sang "what belongs to him or her and to none else."
6. Various answers possible

Question on "My Faith Looks Up to Thee"

Guilt, a fainting heart, confusion, and death

Lesson 44

1. Sam Houston
2. To be annexed for the purpose of becoming a state
3. A letter by John Calhoun supporting slavery
4. Democrat: James K. Polk, Whig: Henry Clay
5. The U.S. and Great Britain agreed to divide the territory at the 49th parallel.
6. Texas was annexed in March and became a state in December.
7. Polk claimed that American troops were fired upon on Texas soil, but Mexico disputed that the land really belonged to Texas.
8. 1846, 1848
9. Texas, California, and the land in between for $15 million
10. Texas practiced slavery, and many Americans objected to the admission of another slave state.

Questions on the Poems by Emily Dickinson

1. Not having to be somebody "to an admiring bog"
2. It makes them more precious and special.
3. Nothing
4. It takes one to distant lands.
5. If she is able to help others

Question on "O Holy Night"

Dealing with sin, personal identity and worth, having a friend in trials, relationships among people

Lesson 45

1. Our country started with a protest; we have seen many protests in our history (civil rights and Vietnam, for instance)
2. Moses, Nathan, the prophets
3. By clearing the sellers and moneychangers from the temple
4. Protests against Moses' leadership; the elders rejecting Samuel's sons and wanting a king; Jeroboam's rejection of Rehoboam's authority
5. Yes
6. Christians must follow God. When that leads to disobeying man, Christians must accept the consequences.
7. Protest can cause people to realize that laws, conditions, or practices should change; and protests can lead to such changes.

Questions on "Civil Disobedience"

1. The one that governs least or not at all
2. Because they are the strongest
3. Their acceptance of and participation in slavery
4. People in Massachusetts benefit economically from the products of slavery.
5. In prison
6. What the governed person consents to give
7. Answers will vary

English Questions

1. Appeals to emotion: Webster appealed to fears of a difficult future in the U.S.; Holmes appealed to the shame of scrapping the *Constitution*; Thoreau appealed to anger at slavery.
2. Appeals to reason: Webster showed the illogic of nullification; Holmes showed how scrapping the ship didn't make sense; Thoreau showed the inconsistency of opposing slavery but accepting the fruits of slavery.
3. How is each effective: Webster would be effective for people with a sense of history; Holmes would appeal to people with pride in history and the Navy; Thoreau was appealing to those concerned about justice.
4. Which is most effective: answers will vary

History Quiz on Unit 9

1. N; 2. G; 3. J; 4. O; 5. C; 6. M; 7. K; 8. F; 9. B; 10. D; 11. A; 12. I; 13. L; 14. H; 15. E

Unit 10

Lesson 46

1. Yes
2. The New Testament tells slaves to respect their masters and masters to treat slaves kindly. Christian slaves and masters were to see each other as brothers in Christ. The teachings of Jesus eventually led to the abolition of slavery.
3. It was not race-based. Slaves were usually captives from war. Many were well-educated and held positions of responsibility for their masters.
4. Horrible conditions on slave ships.
5. They were considered property and had no legal rights.
6. Beaten and given other severe punishment, families separated, sexual exploitation
7. Many slaves accepted the gospel. They saw themselves as being like the Israelites in Egypt.
8. With prejudice and discrimination. Some were seized as suspected slaves.
9. It was dehumanizing for all involved.
10. Not to talk about it.

Bible Question

Philippians 3:2-11—(1) Answers might include: right family, right nationality, hard worker, good reputation, right educational background, appearance, financial status. (2) They are shallow because they do not deal with the inner person and they are all subject to perishing. They are not things that God considers important.

Lesson 47

1. As a state issue, not a Federal one
2. To resettle slaves in Africa
3. *The Manumission Intelligencer, The Genius of Universal Emancipation*
4. *The Liberator*; its tone was uncompromising in calling for immediate abolition
5. Gabriel, Denmark Vesey
6. A rebellion by slaves in Virginia in which the slaves killed many whites
7. To defend slavery more and to limit the rights of free blacks
8. Elijah Lovejoy
9. Over how and whether to include women in the movement
10. Gradual, which was frustrating to many abolitionists; but it did have an impact.

Questions on "To the Public" (from the first issue of *The Liberator*)

1. With indifference
2. Apathy, prejudice, contempt for abolitionists
3. He says it was wrong and he apologizes for it.
4. He advocates immediate liberation and enfranchisement of slaves.
5. He does not intend to be moderate in his arguments.

Questions on "Bury Me in a Free Land"

1. In a land that practices slavery
2. Hearing the steps of slaves or a mother's wild shriek
3. It reflects the abuses and trials they suffered.
4. The ending of slavery in the U.S.

Bible Question

Luke 16:19-31—We can avoid living for self and our own comforts. We can realize that the opinions of others can change. We can understand the passing nature of everything in this world. We can devote ourselves to seeking what is important to God.

Lesson 48

1. Population spread west, and cities grew.
2. Manufacturers produced machinery that helped farmers.
3. The steel-tipped plow, the reaper, and the cotton gin
4. It spread west, taking the plantation system and slavery with it.
5. Lowell, Massachusetts
6. People, especially young women, left home to work in the mills.
7. By organizing unions
8. Government assistance
9. Lecture halls, theaters, gambling, boxing, circuses, horse racing
10. White performers in blackface portraying blacks

Bible Question

John 19:10-11—Pilate appeared to have more power than Jesus, but Jesus had a relationship with God. At the time, Caesar had more earthly power and more followers. We now see Jesus as more successful because His cause continues while the Roman Empire is gone. Rome existed for worldly power, which is passing, while Jesus lived for eternity.

Lesson 49

1. Many came because of the potato famine in Ireland.
2. The Roman Catholic parish church
3. By giving them favors in exchange for their votes
4. Education, professional status, often having a good bit of money
5. To the Midwest and plains states
6. Most did not go to the South because it was far from where they came to the U.S., they did not want to do farm work, and they would have had to compete with slave labor.
7. They were suspicious of the immigrants' cultural and religious differences from most Americans and they feared that the immigrants would work for less pay.
8. The Know-Nothing party
9. A belief that formal schooling provided an opportunity for people to better themselves economically and would improve the nation by reducing crime and ignorance
10. Sabbath-keeping, the outlawing of duels, reform of prisons and institutions for the mentally ill, the abolition of slavery, and temperance

Questions on the Seneca Falls Declaration

1. Strident and insistent
2. Answers will vary.
3. Reference to Nature's God; God as Creator gave inalienable rights; right to pursue happiness dictated by God; God assigns sphere of action; God intended woman to be man's equal and gave woman the same capabilities as man. Legitimate appeals are supported by Scripture.
4. Answers will vary.

Bible Questions

1. Economic success in America led to inequality between rich and poor, the rich using workers for their own gain, pressures to succeed financially, and leisure time that was sometimes spent in sinful activities.
2. Immigrants might have come to define success as achieving the American way of life (socially and economically), although some probably defined it in terms of personal, political, and religious freedom.

Lesson 50

1. Faithfulness
2. History considers Egypt a great civilization, but the Bible portrays it as the place of slavery and an enemy of God.
3. Saul looked impressive physically but he was a failure spiritually.
4. By whether or not they were faithful to God
5. Israel is central to the Bible but was a relatively minor country in the ancient world.
6. Rome is the great harlot and the persecutor of the church.
7. He looked successful in worldly terms but was a failure spiritually.
8. Answers will vary
9. God considers the heart and whether people are faithful to Him.
10. Answers will vary.

Questions on "The Great Stone Face"

1. The Old Man of the Mountain in New Hampshire
2. Ernest; he wanted to be earnest in his life.
3. That someone would come along one day who would be the "greatest and noblest personage of his time" and who would look like the Great Stone Face
4. The rich Gathergold, the soldier Old Blood and Thunder, and the statesman Old Stony Phiz
5. The poet
6. His life did not match up with the words he had written.
7. Ernest
8. He did not think that he deserved the honor, and he hoped that another would come along to fulfill it.
9. How people usually define success often involves things that are not truly worthwhile.
10. Just like Ernest believed the prophecy and took on the hoped-for characteristics of its fulfillment, so we can become like Christ if we continually look on Him and learn from Him.

History Quiz on Unit 10

1. c; 2. d; 3. b; 4. d; 5. d; 6. a; 7. c; 8. a; 9. a; 10. b

History Test on Units 6-10

1. New York City
2. 1789
3. State, Treasury, War
4. The Cabinet
5. Assumption of national and state debts, a national bank, and a protective tariff
6. Neutrality
7. Forcing sailors from the ships of other countries into duty on one's own ships; especially practiced by the British against American sailors
8. John Adams
9. An attempt by French diplomats to obtain a bribe from American representatives in order to negotiate with the French government
10. To limit the number of potential Republican voters; it harmed the Federalist party.
11. To limit criticism of the Adams administration in newspapers
12. The election of Thomas Jefferson as President as representative of the common man
13. John Marshall
14. The Massachusetts state constitution
15. Federalists, Republicans
16. Virginia and Kentucky Resolutions
17. The Louisiana Purchase
18. Lewis and Clark
19. John Marshall
20. The Court had the right to determine whether a law was constitutional.
21. The power of a state to tax a Federal entity (in this case, a branch of the Bank of the United States)
22. France and Great Britain
23. New England
24. The West
25. War Hawks
26. Baltimore, Maryland
27. The Battle of New Orleans
28. Missouri would be admitted as a slave state, Maine would be admitted as a free state, and slavery would be prohibited in the Louisiana Territory north of Missouri.
29. Monroe Doctrine
30. Secretary of State
31. Andrew Jackson
32. Apparently Henry Clay agreed to support John Quincy Adams for President, in return for which Adams named Clay to be Secretary of State.
33. They got married before Rachel was divorced from her first husband.
34. The policy by Jackson to fill government positions with his supporters
35. State banks that received deposits of Federal funds after the Bank of the United States closed
36. Removing Indians from their lands east of the Mississippi River to land west of the Mississippi
37. Martin Van Buren
38. The Panic of 1837
39. The belief that it was obvious that the destiny of the U.S. was to control the expanse of the continent from coast to coast
40. Independence from Mexico, the Battle of the Alamo, the Battle of San Jacinto, annexation by the United States, statehood
41. James K. Polk
42. To resettle slaves in Africa
43. Because of the potato famine in Ireland
44. The Know-Nothing party
45. Lowell, Massachusetts
46-50. Washington, John Adams, Jefferson, Madison, Monroe, John Quincy Adams, Jackson, Van Buren, Harrison, Tyler, Polk

English Test on Units 6-10

1. N; 2. J or O; 3. D; 4. A; 5. J or O; 6. E; 7. M; 8. G; 9. F; 10. B; 11. C; 12. H; 13. K; 14. I; 15. L

16. Stanza
17. Meter (or scansion)
18. Alliteration
19. Iambic pentameter
20. Henry David Thoreau

Bible Test on Units 6-10

1. American organizations were begun distinct from their British counterparts.
2. Civil religion is a belief system that blends love of country, belief in God, and trust in God's guidance of the United States. People from diverse Christian backgrounds—and even those from other religious backgrounds—can accept it.
3. Thomas Jefferson
4. Timothy Dwight
5. It hindered religious activity.
6. Cane Ridge
7. Second Great Awakening
8. To do away with them and be simply Christians
9. Transcendentalism
10. The millennium or the second coming of Christ

11. Joseph Smith
12. The second coming of Christ
13. Utopian
14. He drove out the sellers and moneychangers.
15. Faithfulness

Unit 11

Lesson 51

1. A commitment to the Union
2. New England during the War of 1812
3. Farmers
4. About one-fourth
5. Plantation agriculture, especially farming
6. Plantation overseers, small farmers, skilled workers, and shopkeepers
7. A majority of white southerners supported slavery.
8. Petitions to abolish slavery in the District of Columbia. The House adopted a gag rule to kill such petitions.
9. A proposed amendment that would forbid slavery in any territory gained by the U.S. from the appropriation to negotiate with Mexico.
10. Popular sovereignty: letting people of a territory decide whether the territory would be slave or free

Bible Questions

Romans 12:3-8. (1) An attitude of humility. (2) An analogy of the body. (3) We can recognize and honor the differences among us as we use our various gifts to serve others.

Lesson 52

1. The discovery of gold in California
2. He supported California becoming a free state.
3. The right to take slaves into all territories
4. California would be admitted as a free state; Utah and New Mexico territories would be organized and would decide for themselves about slavery; a border dispute between Texas and New Mexico would be settled in favor of New Mexico but Texas would receive compensation from the Federal government for pre-admission debts; the slave trade would be abolished in the District of Columbia; a tougher Fugitive Slave Law would be enacted.
5. Henry Clay

6. He supported them.
7. The proposals were presented as individual bills and different coalitions supported them.
8. It applied to any slave who had ever run away, and it forced northerners to assist in something to which they were morally opposed.
9. Franklin Pierce, Democrat
10. The Whig party died out after the election.
11. Stephen Douglas
12. For them to decide on slavery by popular sovereignty
13. Proslavery and antislavery forces fought each other.
14. Charles Sumner
15. He was attacked by Preston Brooks, a congressman and a nephew of South Carolina Senator Andrew Butler.

Questions on "Crime Against Kansas"

1. At the center of North America
2. People who oppose slavery are being forced to accept slavery.
3. He strongly condemns Butler and is mocking and denigrating toward him.
4. As being loyal to a harlot
5. Kansas will be a "ministering angel" when South Carolina "lies howling."

Bible Questions

Romans 14:1-23: (1) Accept those who have different opinions. (2) Different opinions about eating meat and observing special days. (3) All Christians answer to the Lord. (3) Not to cause a brother to stumble. (4) We would be more likely to accept those who have different ideas and not be so quick to divide over relatively minor matters.

Lesson 53

1. Kentucky
2. Compromises
3. Secretary of State
4. New Hampshire and Massachusetts
5. Oratory
6. Secretary of State
7. South Carolina
8. Slavery
9. Secretary of State
10. The presidency

Questions on the Speeches by Henry Clay, Daniel Webster, and John C. Calhoun

1. The Union
2. Those who promote disunion
3. Peaceable secession
4. Liberty and Union
5. Discontent regarding the South over slavery and the loss of equilibrium between slave and non-slave states
6. To protect the rights of the South regarding slavery

Bible Questions

1 Corinthians 12-13: (1) The Holy Spirit. (2) For the common good, or to build up one another. (3) An analogy of the members of the human body. (4) All are necessary; the parts that are not as obvious have vital purposes; the different parts help and support each other. (5) The way of love.

Lesson 54

1. A statement of the interest by the U.S. in purchasing Cuba
2. James Buchanan, Democrat
3. John C. Fremont, Republican
4. An Army officer had taken his slave, Dred Scott, into a free state and a free territory. Scott later sued to obtain his freedom on the grounds that his residence in free areas made him free.
5. The Court said that Scott was not a citizen and thus did not have the right to sue; that blacks were not citizens; and that the Missouri Compromise had denied citizens of their right to property by declaring certain areas as free and thus was unconstitutional.
6. The decision strengthened the belief of pro-slavery men that antislavery forces were trying to rob them of their constitutional rights. On the other hand, it affirmed to opponents of slavery their belief that the Federal government was controlled by people who wanted to protect and extend slavery.
7. The U.S. Senate race in Illinois in 1858
8. Douglas was chosen by the Illinois legislature.
9. The U.S. military arsenal at Harper's Ferry, Virginia.
10. Washington, John Adams, Jefferson, Madison, Monroe, John Quincy Adams, Jackson, Van Buren, Harrison, Tyler, Polk, Taylor, Fillmore, Pierce, Buchanan

Questions on the "House Divided" Speech

1. When he was accepting the Republican nomination to run for U.S. Senator from Illinois in 1858
2. Either slavery will end or it will spread to all the states
3. He says the tendency is toward the spread of slavery.
4. A caged and toothless lion
5. He is very confident of victory.

Bible Questions

1. 1 Peter 3:7—Since men and women are different physically, emotionally, and in the way they think, husbands should accept these differences, appreciate them, and cherish their wives for who they are.
2. 1 Peter 4:10-11—Christians have different gifts, and they should use their gifts to honor God and to bless others.

Lesson 55

1. Appearance, family backgrounds, ethnic and national backgrounds, experiences, male and female differences, and personality differences
2. When there is jealousy and suspicion because of differences; when two countries differ and start a war, or when Christians do not get along and judge each other
3. When people appreciate the value of others who are not like them, when people grow from being with others who are different, and when differences result in a more well-rounded group
4. The Jew-Gentile split
5. Because God gives unity
6. When sin is present; when someone is teaching what is false
7. Accept one another as valuable and see how each contributes to the body and to its mission
8. By accepting those who have different views and being sure that you are not a cause of stumbling to others
9. People have differences of opinion about what is a difference of opinion. Christians often see their own opinions as truth and thus cannot accept those who differ with them.
10. With the world divided in so many ways, Christian unity is a powerful way to say that the gospel can make people different.

Questions on *Uncle Tom's Cabin*

1. Tom's first owner
2. Slave who is sold twice and finally killed
3. Slave woman who escapes to freedom
4. Tom's second owner, lives in Louisiana; dies before he is able to free Tom
5. Tom's cruel final owner
6. Condescending, hateful toward slaves; see selves as powerless to do anything about slavery
7. Many are helpful, but some do not want to help slaves
8. Accepting, eager to escape, fearful
9. To shock northerners into action by showing them how slavery really was
10. She believes that it is wrong and needs to change.
11. Right attitudes about slavery and blacks; prepare them for self-government; colonization in Africa

History Quiz on Unit 11

1. I; 2. G; 3. H; 4. F; 5. E; 6. D; 7. B; 8. A; 9. C; 10. J; 11. S; 12. T; 13. R; 14. O; 15. Q; 16. P; 17. L; 18. K; 19. N; 20. M

Unit 12

Lesson 56

1. Was the main issue slavery or states' rights? Was the main question slavery in the territories or in the states? Should slavery be abolished or expanded? What should be the goal of Federal policy on slavery: protection, abolition, or limitation?
2. Southern Democrats walked out. Northern Democrats nominated Stephen Douglas, while southern Democrats nominated John Breckenridge.
3. Chicago; Abraham Lincoln
4. He was perceived as being too strongly against slavery.
5. John Bell, the Constitutional Union party (made up mostly of former Whigs)
6. He had served in the Illinois state legislature and one term in the U.S. House, and he had run for U.S. Senator against Stephen Douglas.
7. Abraham Lincoln
8. It seceded from the Union.
9. Mississippi, Florida, Alabama, Georgia, Louisiana, and Texas (other states followed later)

10. Montgomery, Alabama; Jefferson Davis as President, Alexander Stephens as Vice President

Questions on the Constitution of the Confederate States of America and the "Cornerstone Speech"

1. It was outlawed.
2. Slavery was guaranteed in those areas.
3. They should be paid for by the states in which they were to be built.
4. Cabinet members and heads of executive departments could also serve in the Confederate Congress.
5. The idea that blacks were inferior to whites

Bible Questions

These questions might be difficult to answer since they involve using principles from Scripture that do not directly address the issue. The questions are, however, good ones to think about.

Lesson 57

1. Proposals to guarantee slavery where it existed and to allow it in territories south of the 36°30' parallel
2. An amendment which guaranteed slavery where it then existed
3. He said that he did not have the authority to do anything about slavery where it existed, and he said he believed that secession was wrong.
4. The people of the country, especially those of the South
5. An attempt to resupply the fort
6. His call for 75,000 volunteers to join state militias
7. South Carolina, Mississippi, Florida, Alabama, Georgia, Louisiana, Texas, North Carolina, Arkansas, Tennessee, and Virginia
8. Delaware, Maryland, Kentucky, Missouri
9. The mountainous region where slavery was rare
10. By using every means he could, including suspending the writ of habeas corpus and putting Confederate supporters in jail

Questions on Abraham Lincoln's First Inaugural Address

1. He said that it had not changed.
2. He said that he would enforce the law.

3. He said that some of them might secede from the Confederacy.

4. One section of our country believed slavery was right and ought to be extended, while the other believed it was wrong and ought not to be extended.

5. Better thinking than had been used up to that time

Bible Questions

In the Old Testament, God sometimes commanded Israel to go to war. However, the prophets spoke of a day in which war would cease (for instance, Isaiah 2:4). Jesus spoke of turning the other cheek and loving one's enemy (Matthew 5:39, 44). Paul urged prayers for government leaders so that people could live in peace (1 Timothy 2:1-2). God was accomplishing His will for the nation of Israel, while Jesus was speaking of interpersonal relationships. The situations are not directly parallel. As Christians, we should take our pattern for life primarily from the New Testament.

Lesson 58

1. North: 23 million; South: 11 million (including four million slaves)

2. About 100,000

3. Most were Protestant; most of the free population was descended from the British or from western or northern Europeans; they spoke the same language; and they shared intangible values such as a commitment to democracy, a pioneer spirit, and faith in and pride in America.

4. He could not fight against Virginia.

5. The pain was deep on both sides, it affected so many people, and the positions were strongly held (and are still held today by many).

6. The North had more manufacturing and railroads, better finances, and was able to continue farming.

7. North: a standing Army and Navy, more population to draw from, better equipped; South: better officers, a captive work force that freed men to fight, only having to fight a defensive war on their home turf

8. Eleven in the Confederacy, 23 in the Union

9. Draft laws in both the North and the South allowed men to pay a fee or hire a substitute to fight for them.

10. Answers will vary.

Bible Question

Good that has come from these wars: American Revolution—a country was begun that offered religious freedom; World War II—aggression and killing were stopped and a zeal for missionary work was ignited; Vietnam—the U.S. learned that its power had limits, and some in Vietnam became Christians; war on terrorism—the killing of innocent people has been resisted.

Lesson 59

1. Blockade the southern coast; defend Washington D.C. and attack Richmond, VA; divide the Confederacy along its major rivers

2. To hold the Union to a stalemate that would lead to more favorable events

3. They hoped that the Confederacy would be recognized by Britain or France and receive aid from them, and they hoped that the North would tire of the war and want a negotiated peace.

4. Bull Run (Manassas Junction); Confederate victory

5. Admiral David Farragut

6. By establishing a long line of defense along the northern Tennessee border in western Kentucky, across the Mississippi, and into Arkansas

7. Virginia and Tennessee

8. U.S. Grant

9. Fort Henry and Fort Donelson

10. "Unconditional Surrender"

Bible Questions

Answers will vary.

Lesson 60

1. Exodus 20:13, Isaiah 2:4, Matthew 5:39-44 and 26:52

2. Conquering the Promised Land (Joshua 1:5, 6:21). Samuel finishing the job that Saul had failed to do (1 Samuel 15:9, 32-34). Sometimes the Lord told David to pursue and defeat his enemies (1 Samuel 30:7-8). The passage that praises the one who attacks Babylon and "who seizes and dashes your little ones against the rock" (Psalm 137:9).

3. Jesus said to love one's enemies and turn the other cheek when offended (Matthew 5:39-44). Paul said that the government does not bear the sword for nothing (Romans 13:4). Revelation describes the fall of Rome, which came at the hands

of a conquering army, as a great victory for God over that evil empire (Revelation 18:1-8).

4. When the church began, Christians were not allowed to serve in the Roman army. After Christianity became the official religion of Rome, soldiers had to be Christians.

5. Wars fought for national pride or for the purpose of aggression and acquisition of land

6. Because peaceful conditions are the best way for people to hear the gospel and be saved

7. Examples of courage and sacrifice; stopping evil; encouraging people to spread the gospel

8. They should leave the issue to the individual's conscience.

9. Desmond T. Doss Sr.

10. Answers will vary.

History Quiz on Unit 12

1. d; 2. b; 3. c; 4. a; 5. c; 6. c; 7. a; 8. d; 9. b; 10. a; 11. c; 12. b; 13. c; 14. a; 15. d; 16. b; 17. d; 18. d; 19. a; 20. b

Unit 13

Lesson 61

1. Washington, Richmond

2. Moving his troops by ship to the end of the peninsula between the James and York Rivers

3. Corinth, Mississippi

4. Albert Sidney Johnston

5. More than the casualties during the Revolutionary War, War of 1812, and Mexican War combined.

6. Antietam (Sharpsburg)

7. Rosecrans (Union) and Bragg (Confederate)

8. a. Union; b. Confederacy; c. Union; d. Confederacy e. Union

Bible Questions

Luke 7:2-10—The centurion was well-respected in the community. He showed humility in that he did not consider himself worthy enough to go to Jesus or for Jesus to come to his house. Jesus said that the centurion showed greater faith than any Jesus had seen in Israel.

Lesson 62

1. Immediate emancipation and integration into white society; allowing slavery in the states where it existed but not extending it to the territories; end slavery but not integrate former slaves into white society

2. To boost Union morale; to make the war a crusade against slavery, thus dissuading Great Britain and France from helping the Confederacy

3. To the states in rebellion (not in border states or in areas controlled by Union army)

4. Almost 200,000

5. He circled around and besieged it from the east, pinning the Confederates against the Mississippi River.

6. To relieve pressure on Vicksburg, to gain recognition for the Confederacy; perhaps to win the war

7. At the dedication of the Gettysburg National Cemetery

8. a. Union; b. Confederacy; c. Union

Questions on the Emancipation Proclamation and the Gettysburg Address

1. The immediate abolition of slavery in those states and parts of states still in rebellion.

2. Whether the states were fairly represented in Congress

3. As commander-in-chief of the Army

4. An act of justice, warranted by the Constitution, upon military necessity

5. The considerate judgment of mankind, and the gracious favor of Almighty God

6. 87 years earlier (fourscore and seven years), in 1776

7. The men who had fought there

8. To be dedicated to the unfinished work of restoring the Union

9. Government of the people, by the people, for the people.

Questions on "The Man Without a Country"

1. Philip Nolan

2. May 11, 1863

3. Treason, for his involvement with Aaron Burr's plot

4. At the trial, he said that he didn't want to hear of the United States again; and the judge granted his request.

5. He was kept at sea, transferred from ship to ship; newspapers were censored; and no one was allowed to talk to him about the United States.

6. Danforth

7. Answers will vary

Bible Question

Luke 23:47—The centurion at the cross praised God and said that he believed Jesus was innocent.

Lesson 63

1. Grant
2. Sherman
3. Andrew Johnson
4. George McClellan
5. Middle Tennessee: Franklin and Nashville
6. Appomattox Court House, Virginia
7. Lincoln wanted to make it relatively easy for states to come back in; Radical Republicans wanted to punish the South.
8. April 14, 1865, Ford's Theater, Washington, D.C.
9. John Wilkes Booth
10. Vice President Johnson and Secretary of State Seward

Questions on Abraham Lincoln's Thanksgiving Proclamation and his Second Inaugural Address

1. Of our own household
2. The cause of freedom and humanity
3. One side would make war rather than let the nation survive; and the other would accept war rather than let it perish.
4. He thought it strange that any men should dare to ask a just God's assistance in wringing their bread from the sweat of other men's faces. He also said that the prayers of both could not be answered and that those of neither had been answered fully.
5. As a judgment for the offense of slavery
6. To bind up the nation's wounds; to care for him who shall have borne the battle, and for his widow, and his orphan—to do all which may achieve and cherish a just and a lasting peace, among ourselves, and with all nations.

Questions on "O Captain! My Captain!"

1. Lincoln is portrayed as a ship's captain who has died just as the ship has come into the harbor.
2. It should be a time of rejoicing, but instead it is a time of sorrow.
3. Shock, anguish, confusion, sorrow, sadness in the midst of joy

Bible Questions

Acts 10:1-48—Cornelius is described as a devout, God-fearing man who helped the Jewish people and prayed to God continually. Cornelius fell down and worshiped Peter and said that he was waiting to hear all that Peter had been commanded by the Lord. Cornelius and the others listening received the Holy Spirit and were baptized.

Lesson 64

1. Volunteering
2. Strongly resisted
3. Running homes and farms, working in factories, teaching school, helping with medical needs, as spies, by disguising themselves as men and serving as soldiers.
4. It helped the Northern economy: greater industrial output and farm production
5. It devastated the Southern economy: loss of farms, railroads, cities; loss of wealth in expenditures and land values.
6. Vice President Stephens and many others opposed Jefferson Davis' administration; Lincoln was assailed from all sides, some wanting him to do more, some wanting him to do less.
7. Taxes, printing greenbacks, issuing bonds
8. Taxes, loans, printing money
9. Great Britain and France
10. Peace Democrats in the North; more broadly, any northerner sympathetic to the South.

Bible Question

Acts 11:1-18—Jewish believers in Jerusalem did not like the fact that Peter went to uncircumcised men and ate with them. Peter explained that it was all done by God's leading and so it had to be right.

Lesson 65

1. Lee, Jackson, Beauregard, Leonidas Polk
2. Bibles, Testaments, and tracts
3. Prayer meetings, revivals
4. Gambling, drinking, swearing, etc.
5. They quit meeting; some never reopened.
6. The belief among southerners that the defeat of their cause proves its righteousness, just as Jesus was crucified despite his being righteous.

Questions on *Company Aytch*

1. He makes fun of all the speeches and politicians
2. Monotony of camp life, uncleanness, missing home; he endured the horrors of war
3. Dirty, mundane, many shortages, kidding among the troops, religious meetings, etc.
4. Seeing friends and others killed; disease, vermin, etc.
5. Trying to eat a rat; getting some corn to eat, etc.
6. He says the cause was lost from the start and that the nation is one and undivided.
7. Various answers possible
8. An individual soldier's perspective on war is different from that offered by a general or from looking at the army as a whole.
9. War is not all glory and battle; in fact, relatively little of it is. Most of the time a soldier has it pretty rough, but even so happy times and an outlook of faith are possible.

History Quiz on Unit 13

1. F; 2. D; 3. G; 4. E; 5. C; 6. B; 7. A; 8. N; 9. O; 10. L; 11. J; 12. M; 13. I; 14. K; 15. H

Unit 14

Lesson 66

1. How was the South going to rebuild? What would happen to the southern economy? What was to be done with the newly freed slaves?
2. They had different ideas about how to readmit southern states and showed prejudice toward blacks.
3. Helped the former slaves find food, clothing, shelter, and medical care; distributed land to blacks; helped build schools for blacks
4. They learned skills, how to read, and how to lead others.
5. Churches, fraternal and other organizations.
6. A family lived on another person's land and worked the fields; in return, the family received a share of the crop as payment. It helped keep families together, although it did keep many in poverty.
7. Black codes
8. "State suicide" theory and "conquered provinces" theory
9. Many former Confederate officials and officers.

10. Congress refused to seat any southern senators or representatives.

Lesson 67

1. The Joint Committee on Reconstruction.
2. By guaranteeing their legal rights and voting rights.
3. A state would lose representation in Congress equal to the percentage of adult males who were not allowed to vote.
4. They were not to be honored.
5. The Radical Republicans
6. Race riots in the South, Johnson's intemperate outbursts, lingering concerns about the war
7. Five military districts, each with a military governor and Union troops stationed there
8. Northerners who came south for personal or political advantage or to try to help southerners
9. Southerners who cooperated with the Republicans in power
10. They resorted to violence against blacks and Republicans.

Lesson 68

1. Tailor
2. Military governor of Tennessee
3. The aristocrats and large slaveowners
4. That the president's military orders pass through the General of the Army, who could not leave Washington without the permission of Congress.
5. It forbade the president from firing any appointee that had been confirmed by Congress.
6. The House of Representatives
7. The Senate
8. The law did not apply to Johnson; the law was unconstitutional; what Johnson had done was not an indictable offense in a court of law.
9. One vote short of the two-thirds necessary to remove Johnson from office
10. Johnson did not oppose any further congressional action on Reconstruction. The Radical Republicans lost public support, but Congress continued to control Reconstruction.

Lesson 69

1. It banned slavery in the District of Columbia and in the territories.
2. Increased them
3. President of Washington University

4. He was held for two years and indicted for treason, but he was released on bail and never tried. President Johnson granted him a pardon in 1869.

5. It said that a person could receive 160 acres free by living on it or planting on it for five years.

6. Agricultural and mechanical universities

7. The Federal government operated on a hard money policy. State banks were loosely regulated, and state bank notes varied in their worth.

8. Financing the Union war effort.

9. Federally-chartered banks

10. It provided a sound, stable national currency and stronger banks.

Lesson 70

1. The wall had not been rebuilt.

2. Very important! Nehemiah depended on it and credited God for the good that happened.

3. Nehemiah and the people prayed and then went to work. It is a good illustration of what we need to do every day. It probably isn't good to try to separate the two spheres. Everything is under God.

4. By opposing Nehemiah, ridiculing the work, wanting to meet with Nehemiah, spreading rumors, trying to kill Nehemiah.

5. He shared his vision with the leaders of the people, and they adopted it as their project.

6. With families side by side, building the portion of the wall next to their homes.

7. Some Jews were trying to make a profit from the distress of others. Nehemiah convicted them of their sin and they quit.

8. Self-sacrifice, a clear vision of the goal, dependence on God, not being distracted by opponents

9. He trusted God to take care of him.

10. They were convicted of their sins.

11. They had to be rid of foreigners, restart tithing and Sabbath observances, and put away foreign wives.

12. Various answers possible

English and Bible Question

Like Nehemiah, the Radicals had a clear goal they wanted to implement. On the other hand, the Radicals imposed their plan and did not try to gain the support of the people. They lorded it over the South by forcing their vision on the region.

History Quiz on Unit 14

1. d; 2. c; 3. d; 4. b; 5. a; 6. b; 7. d; 8. b; 9. a; 10. b; 11. c; 12. c; 13. c; 14. b; 15. a

Unit 15

Lesson 71

1. Attended West Point, served in the Mexican War, served at various military posts, resigned his commission because of alcoholism

2. Black voters

3. Denying the right to vote on the basis of race, color, or previous condition of servitude

4. The attempt to corner the gold market, bribery involving selling goods to an Army post, the St. Louis Whiskey Ring, the Credit Mobilier railroad construction scandal

5. The political machine that used corruption to run New York City and skim off large amounts of public money

6. Horace Greeley

7. Paper money issued by the government

8. They made money cheaper and allowed some degree of inflation. Farmers and debtors wanted them used.

9. Blacks were not generally politically active; whites wanted power and were willing to use intimidation to keep blacks out of politics and voting; whites controlled the southern economy; Congress pardoned many former Confederates; there was no widespread commitment to equality for blacks in either the North or the South

10. Washington, John Adams, Jefferson, Madison, Monroe, John Quincy Adams, Jackson, Van Buren, Harrison, Tyler, Polk, Taylor, Fillmore, Pierce, Buchanan, Lincoln, Andrew Johnson, Grant

Bible Question

The world defines success in terms of money, popularity, material accomplishments and possessions, fame, beauty, and sometimes athletic or artistic ability.

Lesson 72

1. The war was over and slavery had been ended; the prospects for settling the west were good; people were gaining a higher standard of living; advances were being made in technology, com-

munication, and transportation.
2. Gold, sliver, and copper
3. Began in Texas; ended in Abilene, Kansas
4. Over 200
5. The Sioux
6. Nine-fold, from 1.1 million to 9.9 million
7. New England and the Middle Atlantic states
8. Eastern and southern Europe, including Italy, the Balkans, Poland, and Russia
9. Public transportation, street lighting, police and fire protection, sanitation
10. African-Americans

Bible Question

Opposite directions: able to own more, but able to go deeper in debt; able to communicate more rapidly and widely, but able to communicate things that are not worth being shared; able to heal people better, but also able to take more lives; able to travel more widely and more rapidly, but often travel for selfish reasons or no reason; able to own more clothes, but often clothes are immodest; other answers possible.

Lesson 73

1. No other single method of crossing the continent conveniently was available; travel between the coasts was slow and often dangerous.
2. New Orleans
3. The Union Pacific and the Central Pacific
4. Eastern: Omaha, Nebraska; Western: Sacramento, California
5. The Union Pacific hired many Irish, and the Central Pacific hired many Chinese.
6. Land grants, loans, and tax breaks
7. May 10, 1869
8. Promontory Point, Utah
9. A trip across the country now took only a week; materials and goods could reach factories and markets; the government carried workers, materials, and the mails cheaply or for free; new markets were opened up and the national economy was stimulated.
10. Excessive profit-taking by the companies; destruction of the buffalo and the Native American way of life.

Bible Question

Answers will vary.

Lesson 74

1. Republican: Rutherford B. Hayes; Democrat: Samuel J. Tilden
2. To recall the horrors of war and blame them on the opposition party
3. Oregon, Louisiana, South Carolina, and Florida
4. Congress appointed a commission that voted 8-7 along party lines for Hayes.
5. Hayes agreed to remove the remaining Reconstruction troops from the South and to appoint a southerner as Postmaster General, and Democrats agreed to withdraw their opposition to Hayes.
6. To be able to control state politics in the South
7. Hayes did the two things mentioned above, but other actions that had been discussed were not taken.
8. Blacks. Neither party defended their rights and they came to be at the mercy of southern Democrats.
9. Democratic state governments in the South limited or removed the civil rights of blacks.
10. Republicans had the most power, but Democrats were not far behind.

Bible Question

Using blessings of progress for good:
transportation and travel—taking the gospel to more people; helping people
communication—teaching the gospel to more people, developing better Bible knowledge
medical and agricultural technology—helping people have a better quality of life
the relative wealth of churches and Christians—using money to support evangelists and missionaries and to help the poor

Lesson 75

1. Going faster
2. Good: better health care, better ability to travel and communicate, slavery had ended, farming techniques were improving; bad: racial prejudice was widespread; industrial workers were paid low wages in unsafe conditions
3. Quality of life issues for babies and the elderly, the cost for such care in terms of money and human effort; questions surrounding stem cell research, etc.
4. Doing research with embryonic stem cells destroys the embryo; the possibility exists of abor-

tions being performed for the purpose of using cells for research or medical treatment.

5. By emphasizing the accomplishments of man and preventing appreciation of God's world

6. We have become better at good things and at bad things.

7. Getting closer to the goals that He wants us to accomplish.

8. To go back to His ways when people have left them

9. By using the principles of God's truth

10. Answers will vary

Questions on *Little Women*

Opinion questions; answers will vary.

History Quiz on Unit 15

1. False; characterized by scandals
2. False; nominee of the Democratic party and of liberal Republicans
3. False; because whites had a lack of commitment to equality for blacks
4. True
5. False; significant conflict
6. True
7. False; Sacramento, California
8. True
9. False; decided by a commission created by Congress
10. True

History Test on Units 11-15

1. One-fourth
2. Petitions calling for the abolition of slavery in the District of Columbia
3. The idea that settlers in a territory should decide whether the territory would be slave or free
4. It included a more stringent fugitive slave law that angered many in the North.
5. Violence between proslavery and antislavery forces in the Kansas Territory
6. Charles Sumner
7. Kentucky
8. New Hampshire and Massachusetts
9. He defended it and saw it as a positive good.
10. It said that blacks could not be citizens.
11. The 1858 U.S. Senate race in Illinois
12. Harper's Ferry, Virginia
13. It divided, and two factions each nominated a presidential candidate.

14. He said that he would not and could not interfere with it in the states but that he opposed its extension in the territories.
15. South Carolina
16. Jefferson Davis
17. The belief that blacks were inferior to whites
18. Fort Sumter, South Carolina
19 & 20. South Carolina, Mississippi, Florida, Alabama, Georgia, Louisiana, and Texas, North Carolina, Arkansas, Tennessee, Virginia
21. Delaware, Maryland, Kentucky, Missouri
22. Blockade the southern coast; defend Washington D.C. and attack Richmond, VA; divide the Confederacy along its major rivers
23. Recognition by Britain and/or France and a negotiated peace with the Union
24. Virginia and Tennessee
25. It led to more states seceding from the Union.
26. Freedom for slaves in those states still in rebellion against the Union.
27. The dedication of the military cemetery at the Gettysburg battlefield
28. William T. Sherman
29. George McClellan
30. Appomattox Court House, Virginia
31. John Wilkes Booth
32. It was strongly opposed in both the North and the South.
33. A man could pay a fee or hire a substitute to avoid serving.
34. Freedmen's Bureau
35. Sharecroppers
36. Laws passed by states to restrict the rights of blacks
37. Many former Confederate officials and officers were among those who had been elected.
38. It abolished slavery.
39. It defined citizenship and the rights of citizens.
40. It guaranteed the right to vote regardless of race or previous condition of servitude.
41. Scalawags
42. His alleged violation of the Tenure of Office Act
43. Tammany Hall or the Tweed Ring
44. Land grant universities that emphasized agriculture and mechanical engineering
45. Greenbacks
46. Union Pacific and Central Pacific
47. Hayes (Republican), Tilden (Democrat)
48. The returns from four states were disputed.
49. Democrats dropped their efforts to get Tilden

elected as president, and Republicans ended Reconstruction in the South.
50. Southern blacks

English Test on Units 11-15

1. Harriet Beecher Stowe
2. Simon Legree
3. She jumped from ice floe to ice floe across the Ohio River.
4. Edward Everett Hale
5. Aaron Burr
6. Yes
7. Walt Whitman
8. The captain of a ship who has died just as the ship reaches harbor
9. Sam Watkins
10. The idea that there is a north and a south
11. Louisa May Alcott
12. Meg, Jo, Beth, and Amy
13. John Brooke
14. Laurie
15. Mr. Bhaer

Bible Test on Units 11-15

1. Race, family background, education, experiences, etc.
2. People can learn from each other, and the group can be stronger if people can offer different abilities.
3. They usually see differences as a reason to be suspicious of others and to separate from those who are different.
4. The Jew-Gentile difference
5. Accept them as the work of the Spirit, use their abilities to bless others.
6. Accept those who see things differently as people who answer to the Lord and not to them
7. With the world divided in so many ways, it is a powerful message when Christians are able to get along.
8. God's commanding Israel to go to war, to conquer the Promised Land, to destroy their enemies, etc.
9. Jesus said to love one's enemies and to turn the other cheek.
10. Peace provides the best conditions for teaching the gospel so that people can be saved.
11. Conscientious objector
12. It provides examples of courage and sacrifice; evil is stopped; those in the military are challenged to think about what is really important;

and people are moved to teach the gospel to those in other lands.
13. Bibles, Testaments, and tracts
14. Preaching, prayer meetings, and revivals
15. The belief among southerners that the defeat of their cause proved its righteousness, just as Jesus was crucified despite His being righteous.
16. The wall had not been rebuilt.
17. Nehemiah
18. He spoke of it as their project; people worked on it regardless of their skills; families worked on the portion of the wall near their homes.
19. Improved medical technology enables longer lives, but such treatment is expensive and requires more care; stem cell research involves questions about destroying embryos, using cells from aborted babies, and other issues.
20. Faithfulness

Lesson 76

1. The Stalwarts and the Half-Breeds
2. He withdrew the last remaining Federal troops from the South.
3. The remaining Republican state governments collapsed and Southern Democrats regained control.
4. Hayes wanted to maintain oversight of Federal elections; he refused to give government jobs as political favors; he opposed labor strikes; he refused to limit Chinese immigration because it would violate a treaty; and he opposed increasing the minting of silver coins.
5. Republican: James Garfield; Democrat: Winfield Scott Hancock
6. He was assassinated in July and died in September.
7. About twelve percent of Federal jobs were to be filled by competitive Civil Service examinations overseen by the Civil Service Commission; the president could increase the positions covered by Civil Service.
8. Republican: James G. Blaine; Democrats: Grover Cleveland
9. Blaine was attacked as being politically corrupt; Cleveland was attacked for being personally corrupt.
10. It was the first presidential election that the Democrats had won since 1856.

Lesson 77

1. He extended the list of Federal jobs to be filled

by civil service examinations, but he also fired thousands of Federal employees and replaced them with Democrats.

2. He opposed most of them.

3. Regulation of the railroad industry and the creation of the Interstate Commerce Commission to investigate and prosecute alleged violators

4. Grover Cleveland, Democrat; Benjamin Harrison, Republican

5. Many Federal workers were replaced with Republicans; the Pension Act was passed for Union Army veterans; tariffs were increased.

6. Conditions of Indians

7. Prosecution of business combinations that resulted in a restrain of trade

8. Silver

9. Democrats gained a large majority in the House and cut the Republican majority in the Senate.

10. The nation was changing from an agricultural society to an industrial one, and this change caused many issues that needed to be addressed.

Bible Question

Psalm 8—The name of God is displayed in creation. The heavens are the work of God's fingers. God created man to rule over the created world.

Lesson 78

1. They were not strong and their bank notes were not reliable.

2. Business was not able to expand, and the gold supply could fluctuate.

3. Federally-chartered banks

4. 16-to-1

5. The U.S. government was to buy between $2 million and $4 million in silver each month.

6. It required that the government buy $4.5 million in silver each month.

7. Bimetallism

8. He wanted it to be repealed.

9. The gold reserve was running low, and the danger was that paper money might not be able to be redeemed in gold as promised.

10. A group of bankers agreed to buy U.S. bonds with gold and to try to stop the flow of gold overseas.

Bible Question

Psalm 139:13-14—Every human is knit together by God in the womb and is a wondrous creation.

Lesson 79

1. Republicans: big businessmen, western farmers, army veterans, blacks; Democrats: southern whites, immigrants, laborers, and some businessmen.

2. To promote business

3. Farmers

4. Lower prices for farm produce; fees charged by elevators, railroads, and middlemen; weather and insect problems.

5. They were traditionally independent and did not live close together.

6. The Patrons of Husbandry, or the Grange

7. Alliances (Northwest and Southern; also Colored)

8. The Populist or People's Party

9. Free and unlimited coinage of silver at the ratio of 16-to-1, electoral reforms, government ownership of railroads and utilities, a graduated income tax, and better working conditions in factories

10. In 1890, Populists won several Senate and congressional seats and governorships. In 1892, they won even more elections. Its presidential candidate received a million popular votes and 22 electoral votes.

Questions on the Populist Party Platform of 1892

1. Moral, political, and material ruin

2. European conditions

3. It says that the issues it talks about should be dealt with first since they will determine whether there is a nation at all.

4. The government

5. It opposes all of them.

Bible Question

Romans 1:20—God's invisible attributes: His eternal power and divine nature

Lesson 80

1. Darwin suggested that variations in living things are hereditary. He said that all living things are in a struggle for survival and that only the fittest survive. He said that living things adapt through the process of natural selection and that change has taken place from simple to complex forms.

2. Assumptions that the earth is billions of years

old; accepting what scientists say without any alternative views being offered; other answers possible.

3. The Bible clearly says that God created the heavens and the earth out of nothing.

4. Theistic evolution accepts God as Creator but says that evolution is the process that has brought the world to the point it is today.

5. The Pentateuch and the Gospels

6. Increased crime rate, depression, abuse, abortion, etc.

7. Evidence for macro-evolution does not exist; no evidence exists for evolution across species; known variations are almost all harmful, not helpful; the geologic column as a whole has never been found; the theory of evolution as held by scientists changes over time; the theory of evolution goes against the laws of thermodynamics; transitional forms have not been found; there is a qualitative difference between man and the rest of creation that evolution cannot bridge.

8. Because people want to find supposed evidence for evolution and ignore the evidence of a Creator

9. Possible ways of handling situations from a materialistic viewpoint:
   a. Since the woman had a limited "quality of life," she could be eliminated.
   b. No ultimate standard would say the boy did anything wrong.
   c. It would seem to be a reasonable proposal.

10. People who believe it trust that it is true without the evidence to support their belief.

Questions on "When I Heard the Learn'd Astronomer"

1. He heard the astronomer going on and on with facts and figures and charts and being applauded by the audience.

2. He went out and wandered by himself.

3. When he would simply look up in silence at the stars

4. The psalm says that the heavens declare the glory of God, even where there is no voice to be heard.

5. Statistical and scientific analysis cannot take the place of simple wonder and amazement at God's creation.

6. Answers will vary.

Questions on *Humorous Stories and Sketches*

1. Men liked to bet on many things, they played tricks on each other, and they liked telling tall tales.

2. Exaggeration and lies, pointed personal attacks, and even physical violence.

3. Answers will vary. Twain takes a common thing (such as barbers or typical human behavior) and exaggerates it for humorous effect.

4. The men marching around and playing soldier is funny until they actually kill someone, which reminds us that the story is about war.

5. He doesn't like it.

History Quiz on Unit 16

1. Stalwarts and Half-Breeds

2. He withdrew the last Federal troops from the South.

3. Chester A. Arthur

4. Civil service

5. A Republican who supported the Democrat Cleveland in 1884

6. He opposed them.

7. Benjamin Harrison

8. The Sherman Antitrust Act

9. The change from an agriculture-based to an industrial-based economy and society

10. Not always very reliable

11. Printing currency and coining silver

12. Populist party

13-25. The first 24 presidents: Washington, John Adams, Jefferson, Madison, Monroe, John Quincy Adams, Jackson, Van Buren, Harrison, Tyler, Polk, Taylor, Fillmore, Pierce, Buchanan, Lincoln, Andrew Johnson, Grant, Hayes, Garfield, Arthur, Cleveland, Harrison, Cleveland

Unit 17

Lesson 81

1. National rail transportation and national communication systems; electrical power; large number of inventions and advances in technology that were applied to industry

2. Individual proprietorship and partnership

3. A business organization chartered by a state government, run by a board of directors, possibly with the sale of stock, and considered a legal person separate from the persons involved in the business

4. Pool, trust, holding company, interlocking directorate

5. Large companies were able to supply and respond to a changing and growing national market; they could use mass production and distribution techniques and technological advances; they could produce products at lower cost which meant lower prices

6. Positive: more goods were available to the public at affordable prices; more Americans were able to find work; negative: lack of competition drove some prices higher and lowered quality; a larger gap developed between rich and poor; workers felt used by their employers.

7. Railroads

8. Vanderbilt: shipping and railroads; Rockefeller: oil

9. The business of managing investments in companies

10. Ward, Sears, and Roebuck

Bible Question

Leviticus 19:9-37—with compassion, consideration, honesty, and love

Lesson 82

1. 59 hours per week; under $500 per year

2. The numbers of workers involved, the traditional American desire to be independent, resistance by and other difficulties with immigrants (such as language barriers), the view by many workers that their current job was temporary, and the suspicion of unions as being socialistic

3. Coal mining

4. Agreements that immigrants would sign to work for a particular company, in return for which the company would pay their passage to America

5. Knights of Labor

6. Eight anarchists

7. By craft (or profession) and by industry

8. Homestead, PA

9. Eugene V. Debs; the Pullman Railroad Car Company

10. Industrial Workers of the World

Bible Question

Isaiah 1:16-17 and Amos 4:1-3—seek justice, defend those who cannot defend themselves, resist oppressing the poor and needy

Questions on the Hymns by Philip P. Bliss

1. God's great light will be shining to bring people to shore, but they need our lower or smaller lights to help them find their way.

2. Serving others, making sure that our lives are truly following Jesus.

3. The writer wants more of those traits that will help him to be like Jesus.

4. Answers will vary.

5. The mighty Son of God was a Man of Sorrows; He bore shame for me; the spotless Lamb made atonement for sinful me; He died but is now in heaven; He is coming again with His ransomed ones.

Lesson 83

1. A South that would be open to industry, that would involve all of its citizens and all of its natural resources, and that would not be as dependent on cotton farming alone.

2. Plantation system gone; plantations broken up into small farms; increased diversity of crops; development of a national market; harvesting of forest products; greater use of machinery and fertilizer; help from agricultural colleges

3. It provided labor for farming, but it kept many people poor and unable to buy much.

4. Building of textile mills and railroads; use of coal and electricity for power

5. More colleges and trade schools were opened.

6. State funding for grade schools did not increase much.

7. Democratic

8. Redeemers or Bourbons

9. They supported industrial growth, but they resisted social changes.

10. Homesteading, mining, conflict between cattle drivers on one hand and ranchers and farmers on the other, the influence of railroads

Questions on "The Significance of the Frontier in American History"

1. The director of the Census Bureau said that there was now no identifiable frontier line of population in the U.S.

2. It had always been the area into which pioneers moved to make new settlements.

3. It helped Americans always envision new possibilities and opportunities; it helped them be adaptable and desire to gain control over nature;

it made ownership of land, the disposition of public lands, and relations with Indians important issues.

4. The first colonists were primarily English; but later immigrants were Scots-Irish (in the South), Pennsylvania Dutch, Scandinavian (in the Midwest), and other ethnic groups; the interior developed an independence from the East Coast.

5. The promotion of democracy in the U.S. and in Europe

Bible Questions

Isaiah 58:6-7—Helping the poor, homeless, and defenseless says that you care about them because God cares about them. Such actions say something about your character. We must be guided by God's character and not society's standards.

Mark 10:23-25—Riches do not necessarily indicate God's approval. God sometimes allows people to accumulate wealth even if they do not follow God's will.

Lesson 84

1. Migration from rural areas, new immigration from overseas
2. Southern and eastern Europe
3. Ellis Island
4. Disease, financial responsibility, if they had jobs or relatives, etc.
5. Prejudice, dangerous jobs, low wages, crowded tenements
6. Chinese
7. Iron and steel frames, elevators
8. Growing urban population, government's friendly attitude toward business, the needs of new immigrants (many of whom were poor)
9. Stereopticon, bicycles, motion pictures, circuses, Wild West shows, vaudeville, music, team sports
10. World's expositions and fairs

Questions on "The New Colossus" and "Casey at the Bat"

1. The old Colossus was a giant that stood astride a harbor with conquering limbs. The New Colossus is a mighty woman with a torch who welcomes exiles from other countries.
2. Their "storied pomp"
3. Tired, poor, huddled masses yearning to breathe free, homeless
4. 4 to 2

5. That one of the batters who came before Casey would make the third out
6. He struck out.

Question on the Hymns by Fanny J. Crosby

Various answers possible

Bible Questions

Matthew 25:31-46—The test is whether people have helped those in need whom they have had the opportunity to help. Church activities are not included (they are supposed to equip us for doing the real work of service in Jesus' name).

Lesson 85

1. The application of the "survival of the fittest" idea to society
2. Herbert Spencer
3. William Graham Sumner
4. It said that the acquisition of wealth was simply an indication that the wealthy were better fitted to have it.
5. They were unfit and should not be artificially helped.
6. The belief that the mission of the church is to address the material needs of people
7. YMCA, Salvation Army, soup kitchens, and advocacy for laws to address social ills such as child labor restrictions
8. Walter Rauschenbusch
9. He said that the kingdom of God was about a better life here on earth, that regeneration was becoming more socially aware, and that salvation was the "voluntary socializing of the soul."
10. Christians are to serve other people, but Jesus and the gospel are primarily about a person's relationship with God and not a person's physical condition.

Questions on "O Master, Let Me Walk with Thee"

1. In service to others, enduring toils and cares, teaching the slow of heart and the wayward, enduring Pharisaical attitudes, when needing patience
2. Answers will vary.

Questions on *In His Steps*

1. Henry Maxwell, Edward Norman
2. Alexander Powers, Donald Marsh
3. The Rectangle
4. Loreen
5. Chicago
6.-10. Answers will vary

History Quiz on Unit 17

1. C; 2. E; 3. B; 4. A; 5. F; 6. D; 7. K; 8. P; 9. Q; 10. T; 11. H; 12. G; 13. S; 14. R; 15. I; 16. M; 17. O; 18. J; 19. N; 20. L

Unit 18

Lesson 86

1. Grover Cleveland
2. The Panic of 1893
3. The Sherman Silver Purchase Act
4. The silver issue and the tariff issue
5. A personal income tax
6. McKinley (Republican) and Bryan (Democrat)
7. Whether to nominate Bryan or choose another candidate.
8. McKinley gave speeches from his front porch while Bryan made an intense tour of the country.
9. Bryan did not do well among laborers, and many blamed the Democrats for the recession.
10. The Dingley Tariff and the Gold Standard Act

Questions on "Cross of Gold"

1. 1896 Democratic National Convention
2. Whether the U.S. should remain on the gold standard or go to a policy of bi-metallism
3. He says that the Democrats support the gold standard but are also open to bi-metallism.
4. He says the U.S. should not wait to see what other nations do but should chart its own course.
5. The gold standard that he says will ruin the working man and family

Questions on "America the Beautiful"

1. Natural beauty, pilgrim ancestors, heroes in war, dreams for the future
2. God shed His grace on the country, God mend our every flaw, God refine our gold

Bible Questions

1. No
2. He is referring to his struggle against sin that he is well aware of.
3. His own giving in to sin

Lesson 87

1. Residency requirements, denial of the vote because of conviction for crimes (sometimes petty), poll tax, literacy test, party primaries, grandfather clause
2. Victims of prejudice, discrimination, and segregation
3. That it only applied to government actions, not to actions by private individuals
4. Separate but equal policy
5. It upheld the practice as a valid use of a state's police powers.
6. Lynching
7. Washington believed that blacks could best help themselves by getting an education, pursuing a trade, and contributing to society in a positive way. He accepted segregation, and he encouraged blacks to do what they could to improve and advance themselves within the system.
8. Du Bois was willing to agitate for such political and social equality.

Questions on the "Speech Before the Atlanta Cotton States and International Exposition" and "Of Booker T. Washington and Others"

1. "Cast down your bucket where you are."
2. The extremist folly
3. That they be prepared for the exercise of these privileges
4. Better to earn a dollar in a factory than to spend a dollar in an opera-house
5. Separate as fingers on the hand but working together as a hand
6. Jefferson Davis
7. Terms such as compromiser, adjustment, and submission
8. Political power, insistence on civil rights, higher education of Negro youth
9. The right to vote, civic equality, and the education of youth according to ability
10. To oppose a part of the work of their greatest leader when he urges accommodation and acceptance of their position in society

Questions on "Sympathy" and "Songs for the People"

1. The aroma coming from a flower bud just opening
2. Because it wants to be free!
3. He feels like a caged bird as a black man in American society.
4. To make songs for people who are weary, poor, and aged, and for little children
5. Peace will encircle the world when men's hearts are more tender.

Bible Questions

1. Through Jesus Christ
2. To set his mind on the things of the Spirit
3. By the Spirit putting to death the deeds of the flesh

Lesson 88

1. It built on the Populist movement; it was a middle-class, urban movement led by young, well-educated people who were politically active.
2. Poor working conditions, corrupt city governments, poor housing
3. Secret ballot, direct party primaries, initiative, referendum, recall, direct election of U.S. senators, off-year elections for states and cities, women's suffrage
4. Commission government and the use of professional city managers
5. Galveston, Texas
6. Child and women's labor, maximum ten-hour workdays, a minimum wage, regulation of monopolies and utilities
7. Prohibition
8. Robert M. LaFollette
9. Theodore Roosevelt
10. Muckrakers

Lesson 89

1. Strong's *Our Country* and Mahan's *The Influence of Sea Power*
2. The whites living there overthrew the monarchy, set up a government, and appealed to the U.S. for annexation.
3. Spanish misrule and a downturn in the sugar industry caused by the American tariff.
4. An insulting letter about McKinley and the blowing up of the USS *Maine*.
5. The Philippines
6. Cuba, the Philippines, Puerto Rico, and Guam. The U.S. also took Wake Island during this time.
7. Some Filipinos tried to run the Americans out.
8. By claiming various spheres of influence in the country
9. The Boxers
10. A combined force of various nations broke the rebellion, and China was ordered to pay indemnities.

Lesson 90

1. Id, ego, superego
2. Irrational
3. Subconscious
4. Jewish
5. None
6. People think in Freudian terms and look for answers in sources other than the Bible. Freud's ideas have been an influence for a materialistic view of people and the world.
7. The Bible says that a person is a spiritual being, created by and responsible to God, with a God-given capacity to determine right and wrong. Freud denied all of this.
8. Yes, but a person is still responsible for his or her actions.
9. It attempts to remove personal responsibility and says that God does not exist.
10. Some people want a reason for not believing in and following God. Christians sometimes want to fit in with their contemporaries, and so they try to adapt the Bible's teachings to conform to contemporary philosophies.

Questions on *Up From Slavery*

1. 1858 or 1859
2. Hampton Institute
3. Under the raised board sidewalk
4. He thought it inhibited the activities of blacks, especially with regard to voting and politics
5. Alabama
6. The North
7. The Cotton States Exposition Address in Atlanta
8. By working hard in their jobs, getting an education, being outstanding citizens, and not being concerned about social integration or revolution
9. He gave them the opportunity to have self-respect, to make something of themselves, and to

believe that America was their country also.

10. Patient, confident, optimistic, hard-working, thankful for his opportunities.

History Quiz on Unit 18

1. Booker T. Washington
2. Theodore Roosevelt
3. William Jennings Bryan
4. Grover Cleveland
5. W. E. B. Du Bois
6. Robert LaFollette
7. William Randolph Hearst
8. William McKinley
9. Bi-metallism
10. Grandfather clause
11. Separate but equal
12. Progressive
13. Muckrakers
14. Poll tax
15. Boxers

Unit 19

Lesson 91

1. 76 million
2. 60 percent
3. 47.3 years
4. First
5. 193,000
6. John Dewey
7. Pragmatism
8. To prepare children to be workers in industry
9. Chautauqua Movement
10. Wire services that could send the same stories to newspapers all over the country

Bible Question

Central Bible doctrines—Wording and specific Scriptures might vary somewhat, but should include ideas about Jesus and the gospel (possible passages include 1 Corinthians 15:1-5 and John 1:1-18), Scripture (2 Timothy 3:16-17), and Bible teachings such as faith (Hebrews 11:6) and the Christian life (Mark 8:34-38). A wide range of topics could be listed as matters of opinion.

Lesson 92

1. Governor of New York
2. He brought representatives from the mine union and from mine owners to the White House to talk. This showed that unions ought to be recognized and respected.
3. Trust-busting
4. The Meat Inspection Act and the Pure Food and Drug Act
5. He wanted them protected and developed carefully. He put much land and resources under Federal control.
6. The Russo-Japanese War
7. Dominican Republic
8. Taft was not the political leader and activist that Roosevelt was. He saw his goal as consolidating and keeping within the law the reforms that Roosevelt started, but not so much initiating new reforms. He was not totally against reforms, however.
9. Taft said he was for tariff reductions, but the bill that passed Congress and that he signed was a compromise that actually raised some rates.
10. Taft appeared to be willing to let public lands be used by private industry, and he fired Forest Service chief Gifford Pinchot during a controversy.

Questions on the Roosevelt Corollary to the Monroe Doctrine

1. He said the United States did not have any land hunger.
2. To see the neighboring countries stable, orderly, and prosperous
3. If the U.S. saw chronic wrongdoing, or an impotence resulting in a general loosening of the ties of civilized society
4. Cuba under the Platt Amendment
5. It would depend upon the circumstances of the case—upon the degree of the atrocity and upon America's power to remedy it.

Bible Question

The church has often conformed to the world in terms of being concerned about appearance, money, and power; the lives of Christians often look much like the lives of people in the world; and as a result the church's influence and ability to help people change their lives has been diminished.

Lesson 93

1. Able to use developments of previous gen-

erations; availability of resources and electrical power; wealth for production and distribution; peaceful conditions for people to make and enjoy these goods

2. Three months

3. Speech, the transmission of sound, and helping the deaf

4. Frank and Charles Duryea

5. Henry Ford

6. Five dollars per day

7. From 8,000 in 1900 to 8.1 million in 1920

8. December 17, 1903

9. Radio (or wireless)

10. Milton Hershey

Bible Question

Some hollow philosophies and deceptions of men include pragmatism, materialism, atheism, New Age doctrines, deceptions of wealth, and so forth.

Lesson 94

1. A railroad

2. The California gold rush

3. Ferdinand de Lesseps

4. Suez is flat and sandy, Panama is mountainous with jungles; Suez is hot, Panama is hot and humid; Panama had deadly diseases.

5. France

6. A poor, unrealistic plan; lack of adequate technology and machinery; high death toll from diseases and accidents; corruption among those in charge of the project

7. The Spanish-American War

8. A revolution in Panama created a new nation there, and the new government wanted to negotiate a deal with the United States.

9. Theodore Roosevelt

10. From 1904 until 1914

Bible Questions

1. Christian businessmen should be honest, kind, treat customers and workers the way they want to be treated, and so forth.

2. Workers should do what is expected of them (and more!) and be honest and trustworthy. If they cannot work in good conscience in a job, they need to find another job or work for themselves. Continuing in a job where they are treated wrongly enables bad behavior by the employer.

Lesson 95

1. Germany

2. They questioned the inspiration and authority of Scripture, they saw Scripture as the product of evolutionary change, and they said it contains the word of God but is not the authoritative Word of God.

3. The account of creation in Genesis and the Gospels

4. Whether He was really divine, whether He actually performed miracles, whether He really was raised from the dead, and whether He is really the exclusive means of salvation

5. Dwight L. Moody and Billy Sunday

6. John Darby and Cyrus Scofield

7. The Church of the Nazarene

8. Holiness and Pentecostalism

9. *The Fundamentals*

10. Prohibition

Questions on *Mama's Bank Account*

1. Because he had enriched their lives by reading aloud to them from classic literature

2. He had paid for the medical care for several children.

3. Mama traded her brooch for it.

4. He let her drink coffee.

5. A sponge soaked in chloroform was put in her box.

6. Doctor

7. Uncle Chris was gruff but generous, Mama could be deceptive sometimes, Katrin adored her mother but could be selfish; other examples possible

8. Determination, fairness, wisdom; other answers possible

9. Being taken by a renter, buying a farm, making arrangements for the reception; other answers possible

10. She could see that through everything their family was strong and God worked everything for good.

History Quiz on Unit 19

1. c; 2. c; 3. b; 4. a; 5. d; 6. c; 7. a; 8. b; 9. a; 10. d; 11. b; 12. d; 13. d; 14. b; 15. b; 16. A; 17. D; 18. E; 19. B; 20. C

Unit 20

Lesson 96

1. Woodrow Wilson (Democratic), William Howard Taft (Republican), Theodore Roosevelt (Progressive)
2. President of Princeton University and governor of New Jersey
3. Congress lowered tariff rates significantly.
4. Personal income tax
5. Federal Reserve System
6. Federal Trade Commission
7. Mexico
8. William Jennings Bryan
9. Charles Evans Hughes
10. "He Kept Us Out of War."

Lesson 97

1. Imperialism, nationalism, national and alliance rivalries
2. Triple Alliance (Central Powers): Germany, Austria-Hungary, Italy; Triple Entente (Allies): Great Britain, France, Russia
3. The assassination of Austrian archduke Francis Ferdinand in Sarajevo, Bosnia in 1914
4. Stalemated trench warfare along a narrow western front near the French-German border.
5. Neutrality
6. Most Americans supported Great Britain and France. German-Americans supported Germany. Irish-Americans disliked the British. Polish and Jewish Americans disliked Russia.
7. Submarine warfare
8. The *Lusitania*
9. Because of a strongly-worded warning by Wilson to the German government
10. A peace without victory, a peace between equals

Lesson 98

1. A note from the German foreign minister to the German ambassador in Mexico, proposing that Mexico enter into an alliance with Germany if the U.S. and Germany should go to war. It suggested that Mexico might win back Texas, Arizona, and New Mexico.
2. April 6, 1917
3. General John J. Pershing
4. By the Selective Service or draft
5. The War Industrial Board, the Food Adminis-

tration, and the Fuel Administration
6. The Committee on Public Information and new laws that forbade criticism of the government
7. The Bolshevik government concluded a separate peace with Germany and pulled out of the war
8. The Fourteen Points
9. November 11, 1918
10. Alvin York

Questions from Wilson's War Message to Congress and his Fourteen Points Speech

1. Because there were serious choices of policy to be made and it was not right or permitted for Wilson to make them himself
2. The U.S. had no quarrel with the German people.
3. Democracy
4. "Open covenants, openly arrived at"
5. A general association or league of nations to guarantee political independence and territorial integrity

Bible Question

The gospel spread to Samaritans, a God-fearing Gentile and his household, and Greeks (or Gentiles), all of whom were people that the Jews disliked.

Lesson 99

1. He asked for a Democratic Congress during the 1918 congressional election campaign; he did not name any Republicans to the peace commission.
2. He was warmly received as a hero and savior.
3. David Lloyd George of Britain, Georges Clemenceau of France, Vittorio Orlando of Italy
4. The expectations created by secret treaties made between countries at the start of the war about how to divide up the conquered nations and their colonies
5. They wanted to make Germany pay and severely limit her power.
6. To see that the League of Nations was included in the treaty
7. It was made to accept the guilt for starting the war, it was forced to pay heavy war reparations, and its army was severely reduced.
8. He compromised on the treatment of Germany and other issues.
9. A secretary-general to administrate, a general

assembly of all nations, a council composed of the Big Five (U.S., Britain, France, Japan, and Italy) to serve permanently as well as other nations on a rotating basis, and other agencies

10. Too hard on Germany, Italy did not get enough, no call for an independent Ireland, the League of Nations would require a continued American commitment in world affairs

11. They opposed it. Henry Cabot Lodge drew up reservations to attach to the treaty.

12. He suffered a stroke.

13. It was defeated twice.

14. Unemployment and an economic slowdown; labor strikes, fears of Communists

Bible Question

Christ enabled people from various ethnic groups to see each other as one new kind of person: Christians.

Lesson 100

1. After the flood, the children of the sons of Noah spread out over the earth.

2. When God confused the languages at the tower of Babel

3. Very little

4. As Jews and Gentiles

5. Descendants of the tribes of the Northern Kingdom and Assyrians who repopulated the area

6. Without stereotypes and prejudices; as individuals

7. "Ethne" means ethnic groups more than it does our modern definition of political entities

8. The preaching of the gospel to Jews from many nations on the day of Pentecost (Acts 2)

9. House churches

10. Pencils

History Quiz on Unit 20

1. S; 2. N; 3. Q; 4. T; 5. P; 6. A; 7. E; 8. B; 9. O; 10. D; 11. R; 12. M; 13. H; 14. G; 15. J; 16. F; 17. I; 18. K; 19. C; 20. L

History Test on Units 16-20

Answers for each paragraph should include:

1. The End of Reconstruction

As part of the outcome of the election of 1876, Democrats gave up the presidential elec-tion in return for Republican agreement to end Reconstruction by removing troops from the South. Democrats were able to regain control of state governments; leaders were called Bourbons or Redeemers. Blacks were generally left out of the political process and out of white society. The New South accepted and encouraged more industry and was less dependent on cotton and agriculture.

2. Reform Movements

Farmers felt left out of American prosperity and felt they were unimportant to the political process. Farmers and farm interests generally led the Populists. They wanted the coinage of silver, government operation of the railroads, a progressive income tax, and electoral reforms. The Progressive movement was more urban-based and carried on the reform banner. Its leaders were better educated and more politically astute. Roosevelt, Taft, and Wilson to greater or lesser degrees supported the Progressive agenda.

3. American Business

Levels of business organization included proprietorship, partnership, corporation, trust (and other combinations). America had the wealth, resources, manpower, and transportation and communication networks to develop national markets. Big business could use new technology and keep costs low. Railroads were the first big business. Labor unions formed to protect and promote the interests of workers, including pay and work conditions. Unions used strikes to get companies to negotiate.

4. City Life

Cities grew by people moving from rural areas and from immigration. Immigration brought new cultures, languages, and challenges to city life. Government services increased to meet the pressing needs of city dwellers. The U.S. was changing from a largely rural to a largely urban population.

5. The Black Experience

Blacks in all areas of the country were the victims of racism, prejudice, segregation, and discrimination. Blacks in the South were victims of violence such as lynching. Blacks were not able to participate in society, education, and government. "Separate but equal" was a common policy, even though what was provided for blacks was usually not equal. Washington was willing to accept social segregation and political inequality if blacks could have the opportunity to work. Du Bois was willing to agitate for greater civil and political rights for blacks.

6. Building a World Empire

Many countries were trying to build overseas empires. Instability in Cuba increased American interest there. The U.S. fought a brief war with Spain and won Cuba and the Philippines as a result. The war increased American interest in a canal through Panama, after the French had failed in their attempt to build one. The U.S. supported a revolution in Panama against Colombia and received the right to build a canal. The American effort lasted ten years and was successful.

7. The Great War

Europe was affected by imperialism, nationalism, and international alliances. The assassination of the Austrian archduke was the spark that started the war. The U.S. was neutral at first, but German submarine warfare against private shipping led to the U.S. entering the war. American involvement helped to end the stalemated trench war in Europe with an armistice. The victor nations met in Versailles to draw up a treaty that included blaming Germany and requiring payment of war reparations by Germany. Woodrow Wilson wanted a League of Nations in the treaty and gave up much to get it. However, the Senate rejected the treaty and the U.S. never joined the League.

8. Presidents: Washington, John Adams, Jefferson, Madison, Monroe, John Quincy Adams, Jackson, Van Buren, William Henry Harrison, Tyler, Polk, Taylor, Fillmore, Pierce, Buchanan, Lincoln, Andrew Johnson, Grant, Hayes, Garfield, Arthur, Cleveland, Benjamin Harrison, Cleveland, McKinley, Theodore Roosevelt, Taft, Wilson

English Test on Units 16-20

Paper should include:

1. Struggle: The struggle in "The Private History" was by Missourians to feel significant in the war and to exert their manhood. They tried to act important but wound up empty and sad. The

Christians in *In His Steps* struggled to do what they believed Jesus would do in business and in society. They achieved much good. Washington's struggle was for economic and educational opportunity for blacks. He achieved great success although blacks were still second-class citizens. In *Mama's Bank Account* the struggle is by immigrants to cope with life in America. Through many trials, they accomplished good because of the strength of Mama's character and of the family.

or

2. Desire: "When I Heard the Learn'd Astronomer" expresses a desire to connect deeply with the reality of nature beyond the cold scientific study of it. "The New Colossus" expresses a desire to welcome immigrants who themselves have a desire for a new start. "Sympathy" is the expression of a desire by blacks to be free from the shackles they feel. "America the Beautiful" expresses the ideals that Americans want their country to fulfill and a desire for God to bless and guide the country.

Bible Test on Units 16-20

Paper should include:

Summaries: Darwin proposed that all living things evolved from simpler forms and are in a struggle characterized by the survival of the fittest. It is an entirely material process. Social Darwinism says that human society is also in a struggle for the survival of the fittest. The social gospel teaches that the church's purpose is to help people live a better life on earth. Freudian psychology holds that people are driven by subconscious desires that come from one's childhood. Liberal theology questions the traditional views of God, Christ, and Scripture and makes faith much more subjective and not as much based on eternal truth.

Impact: Many people have come to accept Darwinian evolution and Freudian psychology as true, and they interpret the Bible and the world in that light. They believe that reality must be filtered through these philosophies instead of through the Bible. Many Christians are involved in helping physical needs and not spiritual needs, although helping with physical needs is one way to help people be interested in the gospel. God is seen as being much less involved in the world (if His existence is admitted at all) by people who accept these theories. Humans and the physical world are sometimes seen as the result of blind chance. Truth is seen as relative and not eternal and permanent. Evangelism is made more difficult because many in the world do not assume the existence of God and do not see why Christian doctrine should be accepted as the only truth.

Unit 21

Lesson 101

1. Democrat: James Cox; Republican: Warren Harding
2. Democrat: Franklin Roosevelt; Republican: Calvin Coolidge
3. The head of the Veterans' Bureau stole medical supplies; the attorney general might have mishandled war reparation payments; the Teapot Dome scandal involved secret deals to tap oil on a government reserve
4. Taxes were cut and tariffs were raised; trade associations were encouraged; the Supreme Court rendered decisions favorable to business.
5. Democrat: John Davis; Republican: Calvin Coolidge
6. Parity
7. The difficulty Germany had in making reparation payments and the loss of trade caused by America's high tariffs
8. They were canceled.
9. Treaties to cut back naval armament, to promise respect for colonial holdings in the Pacific, and to maintain the open door policy in China
10. The outlawing of war except in self-defense

Questions on "The Destiny of America"

1. Looking out for yourself by looking out for your country
2. Righteousness and gain
3. Work with it
4. Through the efforts and character of the individual
5. The spirit of giving one's life for a cause greater than oneself

Bible Question

"Take every thought captive to the obedience of Christ" (2 Corinthians 10:5); remember that "The fear of the Lord is the beginning of knowledge" (Proverbs 1:7); approach the study of science

believing that God created everything and His truth is eternal and must be the standard.

Lesson 102

1. From 106 million to 123 million
2. More people lived in urban areas than in rural areas
3. Immigration was severely restricted during this period.
4. Fear of foreign influences, less need for labor, frustration over immigrants blending in to the U.S. culture
5. Many first and second generation Americans and nationals in other countries resented the changes.
6. Petroleum, natural gas, and electricity
7. It decreased from 12% of the work force in 1920 to 7% in 1930.
8. From 8 million to 23 million.
9. By 1929 over 600 radio stations were in operation and a third of the homes in America had radio.
10. *The Jazz Singer*, 1927

Bible Question

Stay calm, be kind, and be confident in God, whether you understand the issue well or not. Your opponent might be talking loudly to cover his own doubts.

Lesson 103

1. Prohibition
2. It was widely ignored.
3. It went underground
4. Criminals
5. More blacks moved to northern cities
6. The NAACP
7. Marcus Garvey
8. Ku Klux Klan
9. Disillusionment
10. The relativity and quantum theories and the uncertainty principle

Bible Question

Answers will vary. It seems that a Christian should know something about the basic issues involved to be able to state his beliefs and not let attacks go unchallenged.

Lesson 104

1. Democrat: Al Smith; Republican: Herbert Hoover
2. His support for the repeal or cutback of Prohibition and his Roman Catholic faith
3. It created the Democrats' urban base
4. It made loans to farm cooperatives to buy crops off the market when the price was low and put them back on the market when prices were better.
5. Overspeculation in the stock market, especially buying stocks on margin; adjustments in the economy and poor agricultural prices; overproduction relative to consumer ability to buy; wages not keeping pace with production; investment in capital goods decreased; heavy selloff caused losses for those who had bought on margin.
6. October 29, 1929
7. It raised tariffs, which hurt the economy.
8. It made loans to banks and large businesses to keep them afloat.
9. A quicker payment of a bonus that had been promised to them
10. Douglas MacArthur

Bible Question

Challenges include the acceptance of evolution, the denial of the inspiration and authority of the Bible, worldliness, rejection of Biblical morality and absolutes. Christians need to be strong in their knowledge of the Word and in their faith in God. They need to show by their lives that they have a better way to live than what the world offers.

Lesson 105

1. Those who accepted the Bible as literal truth and those who did not
2. The teaching of any theory in public schools that denied God's creation of man as taught in the Bible
3. The ACLU
4. Dayton, Tennessee
5. John T. Scopes
6. Clarence Darrow and William Jennings Bryan
7. When Darrow put Bryan on the witness stand and questioned him
8. Scopes was found guilty and find $100, but the conviction was later reversed on appeal because of a technicality.

9. He died five days later.
10. *Inherit the Wind* (play and movie)

Questions on *Christy*

1. Huddleston
2. Neil MacNeill
3. David Grantland
4. Alice Henderson
5. Fairlight
6. Superstitions, moonshining, family feuds, resistance to change, etc.
7. Helping them see the value of the education; jealousy about the teacher's knowledge; other answers possible
8. Gain: appreciation for others' lives, realizing what you really need to live, etc.; give up: conveniences, comfortable relationships, etc.
9. Various answers possible
10. They would need to see faithful Christian lives.

History Quiz on Unit 21

1. C; 2. E; 3. J; 4. I; 5. G; 6. D; 7. H; 8. F; 9. A; 10. B; 11. L; 12. M; 13. K; 14. O; 15. N

Unit 22

Lesson 106

1. International economic conditions
2. 1920
3. Governor of New York
4. One-fourth
5. New Deal
6. Relief, recovery, reform
7. The brain trust
8. Took the country off the gold standard
9. CCC—Civilian Conservation Corps: cleared forests, built state parks, dams; NRA—National Recovery Administration: regulated business, developed industry codes; AAA—Agricultural Adjustment Act (or Administration): limited farm production, paid farmers for not growing crops.
10. The Works Progress Administration (WPA)—various projects including building or repairing schools, sewage plants, and roads, and funding projects by writers, musicians, and artists

Questions on Franklin D. Roosevelt's First Inaugural Address

1. Fear itself
2. Material things
3. In the joy of achievement and the thrill of creative effort
4. To put people to work
5. Ask Congress to grant him broad executive powers to deal with the emergency

Bible Question

Answers will vary, but might include: Why does suffering exist? Why do innocent people suffer? How can an all-powerful God allow suffering to exist? How can a just God allow good people to suffer and bad people to get away with evil and not suffer?

Lesson 107

1. Tennessee Valley Authority (TVA)
2. Production of electricity, flood control, navigation, soil conservation, recreational lakes
3. Unemployment assistance, disability payments, retirement pensions
4. Taxes on workers and employers
5. It struck down several New Deal measures.
6. Alf Landon
7. He wanted to add a justice for every one over seventy who did not retire.
8. It did not pass Congress.
9. It backfired into Republican victories.
10. The Federal government cut back expenditures.

Bible Question

Hebrews 12:4-11—Discipline (suffering) is from the Lord because He loves us and is training us to maturity. James 1:2-3—We should face trials with joy because testing produces endurance, again helping us to mature.

Lesson 108

1. Huey Long
2. A group formed in 1934 by Republicans and conservative Democrats to oppose what they saw as the New Deal's threat to American liberty
3. A plan to give all retirees sixty and over $200 per month, provided that they not work and that they spend the money within the month
4. Charles Coughlin
5. An area of western Kansas and Oklahoma
6. California
7. Movies and radio
8. *Life*
9. Will Rogers
10. Conservative churches grew while liberal denominations declined.

Bible Question

Answers will vary.

Lesson 109

1. Recognizing the Soviet Union
2. The good neighbor policy
3. Treaties setting tariffs were made with individual countries, and most favored nation status was created.
4. The previous international framework was not strong; internal turmoil in Germany, Italy, and Japan enabled the rise of dictatorships; the alliance among Great Britain, France, and Russia was an uneasy one; France and Britain had allowed their military strength to slip while German power increased; the U.S. removed itself as a player in the international scene; isolationism and pacifism made any move toward increasing armaments politically risky; a complicated web of treaties and alliances drew countries quickly into war.
5. Hitler, Mussolini, Stalin; Japanese militarists
6. Militarizing the Rhineland; taking Austria and the Sudetenland
7. Appeasing Germany
8. Disillusionment over World War I and its outcome, evidence of profiteering from the war
9. Neutrality
10. Great Britain
11. Germany's invasion of Poland on September 1, 1939

Bible Questions

We can live by faith even without all of the answers we would like to have about suffering. There is much we can know, and we can know enough to be saved and to live faithfully for the Lord, but we will not have all the answers in this life.

Lesson 110

1. An irrational process
2. Either He is or He isn't.
3. In such a world, people would not have the opportunity to rise to the occasion in difficulty, show courage, and have other traits that are valuable. Also, in a different world we would not be who we are in this world.
4. We have to trust the God who is even when we don't understand things.
5. God can bring good out of bad.
6. Suffering helps us grow.
7. The righteous will live by faith as unsettling events unfold.
8. Suffering gives us the opportunity to work the works of God.
9. The creation is groaning as in childbirth toward its redemption.
10. God's megaphone to rouse a deaf world

History Quiz on Unit 22

1. False; he blamed it on international economic conditions.
2. False; economic conditions worsened during that period.
3. False; he did not have such a plan.
4. True
5. True
6. False; the NRA approved codes that industries drew up.
7. False; the TVA built dams for electricity, flood control, navigation, and recreation and was involved in soil erosion and conservation projects and other aspects of planning for the Tennessee River Valley.
8. True
9. False; he proposed adding up to six justices for those who did not retire at 70.
10. False; he caused a reaction by opposing Democrats he wanted to see defeated.
11. False; it became more active.
12. False; the hard times brought out advocates of radical ideas.
13. False; the Dust Bowl was a hard hit agricultural area of Kansas and Oklahoma.
14. False; the two popular forms of entertainment were radio and movies.
15. False; he extended diplomatic recognition to the U.S.S.R.
16. False; they seized power undemocratically and were dictators.

17. False; many Americans wanted the U.S. to become less involved in the world.
18. False; his policy was called appeasement.
19. False; Roosevelt wanted to quarantine aggressor nations.
20. False; it started with Germany's invasion of Poland.

Unit 23

Lesson 111

1. Maginot Line
2. Dunkirk
3. The German air attack on Great Britain and the British defense against it.
4. Wendell Willkie
5. He was running for an unprecedented third term as President.
6. The U.S. gave Britain fifty older destroyers in return for the use of British bases in the western hemisphere.
7. The U.S. agreed to lend or lease equipment to any nation resisting Axis aggression.
8. Atlantic Charter
9. A non-aggression treaty
10. December 7, 1941

Questions on the Atlantic Charter and Roosevelt's Declaration of War Speech

1. The right to trade and raw materials
2. The use of force
3. "A date which will live in infamy"
4. The distance of Hawaii from Japan
5. Yes

Bible Questions

The non-material weapons include learning, arguments, conviction, persuasive speech, and so forth. The battle is taking place when Christians train their children and others in the truth of Christ, in making appeals on the basis of the Christian faith in the marketplace of ideas, and so forth. It takes place in one's own mind when a person studies the Word and resists the arguments of Satan. Answers will vary on the last two questions.

Lesson 112

1. "I shall return."

2. Coral Sea and Midway Island
3. Guadalcanal
4. American and British forces caught the Germans between them in a pincer move.
5. Sicily and Italy
6. Tehran, Iran
7. D-Day
8. Thomas Dewey
9. Battle of Leyte Gulf
10. Battle of the Bulge

Bible Questions

God's armor: gird loins with truth—gives solid foundation; breastplate of righteousness—defense against attacks on your heart and vital organs; feet shod with preparation of the gospel of peace—helps you get where you need to go; shield of faith—wards off arrows the enemy shoots at you; helmet of salvation—protects the mind and therefore your entire ability to function; sword of the Spirit, the word of God—what you use to attack the enemy

Lesson 113

1. Yalta
2. The Soviets were given land from Japan and China and the dominant influence in Eastern Europe.
3. V-E Day
4. The atrocities of German concentration camps
5. Iwo Jima and Okinawa
6. Manhattan Project
7. Hiroshima and Nagasaki
8. The courage and sacrifice of the American armed forces and the service and sacrifice by Americans on the home front
9. They were interned in prison camps in the U.S.
10. About 400,000; about fifty million

Bible Questions

Fighting the good fight of faith includes living by faith, standing for the truth, prayer and Bible study, being strong in the grace that is in Christ Jesus, and other matters. You can be in the fight by being respectful of others and aware of your own struggles but firm in your faith in God.

Lesson 114

1. He got a notice from the Army encouraging him to enlist and telling him that he would be drafted if he did not.
2. Medical Corps, Headquarters Company, First Army
3. Governor's Island
4. Five days
5. Bristol
6. The top secret D-Day orders
7. D-Plus 1, or the day after D-Day
8. Dinah Shore
9. To get married
10. The Bronze Star

Bible Questions

2 Timothy 2:1-7—1. A soldier does not need to entangle himself in civilian life; an athlete has to compete according to the rules; a hard-working farmer can receive the bounty of his crop. 2. A soldier might try to carry his civilian belongings with him, or he might be preoccupied with relationships with civilians. 3. A Christian must avoid being entangled with things of the world so that he can serve effectively in the Lord's army.

Lesson 115

1. It was asked of people who were acting in a way that seemed to disregard the war effort.
2. A war between the people of God and the forces of evil, between God and Satan
3. In heaven
4. They do not have a choice; they are in the war.
5. Anything he can to capture souls, including appearing as an angel of light
6. The individual soul, the fellowship of believers, and the world's attack on Christians
7. To sanctify the Lord in our hearts
8. To set apart or make holy
9. The Lord and those who are faithful to Him
10. What side are you going to be fighting on?

Questions on *To Kill a Mockingbird*

1. References to "nothing to fear but fear itself" and "nine old men"
2. Various answers possible
3. Much prejudice and suspicion of new things
4. It is wrong to kill a mockingbird, to condemn Tom Robinson, and to ostracize Boo Radley.

5. It shows Jem and Scout that Atticus can take on challenges and be victorious.

6. Because of the way society treats him

7. He was found guilty.

8. He was killed trying to escape from prison.

9. Various answers possible

10. Various answers possible

History Quiz on Unit 23

1. J; 2. I; 3. F; 4. D; 5. C; 6. E; 7. G; 8. B; 9. H; 10. A; 11. S; 12. T; 13. O; 14. R; 15. M; 16. N; 17. P; 18. L; 19. K; 20. Q

Unit 24

Lesson 116

1. United Nations

2. Security Council

3. U.S., Russia, Great Britain, France, China

4. Role of government, freedom, religion, influence on other countries

5. Controlled Eastern Europe, threatened Turkey and Greece

6. The news that the Soviets had an atomic bomb

7. The Communist forces ran the Nationalist government off the mainland.

8. The U.S. would help people fighting invasion or subversion.

9. A plan to give aid to the struggling national economies of Europe

10. By an airlift

11. North Atlantic Treaty Organization; a mutual defense pact of several North American and European countries

12. The U.N., the Marshall Plan, NATO, and technical assistance to third world countries

Bible Questions

Answers will vary.

Lesson 117

1. Film actors, writers, and producers who were brought before a Congressional committee to find out about their Communist affiliations

2. "Are you now or have you ever been a member of the Communist Party?"

3. Communist and Communist front groups had to register with the Justice Department; anyone who had once been a Communist could not enter the country.

4. Attorney in the State Department and other departments; secretary-general of the U.N. organizing conference; president of the Carnegie Endowment for International Peace

5. That he had once been a Communist agent

6. Hiss sued Chambers for slander.

7. Hiss was found guilty of perjury and sent to prison.

8. That the State Department and other agencies were infested with Communists

9. One of fear and suspicion

10. The Army-McCarthy hearings

Lesson 118

1. Off the China mainland just west of Japan

2. The Soviets controlled the North, while Americans controlled the South.

3. North Korean troops invaded the South to try to reunite the country.

4. It condemned the invasion and asked for troops to repel it.

5. Douglas MacArthur

6. An amphibious landing an Inchon, well behind enemy lines

7. Bomb Communist China north of North Korea

8. It feared bringing Russia and China more directly into the conflict.

9. Truman fired MacArthur.

10. July 27, 1953

Questions "Old Soldiers Never Die"

1. The invasion of Korea by Communist Chinese troops

2. He was informed that reinforcements were not available.

3. Victory

4. 52 years

5. Fade away

Bible Questions

Matthew 22:-15-22—Respect for one's government is an element of a Christian's following the teachings of Scripture, although loyalty to one's country is not the same as loyalty to God. We can be thankful for our blessings in America and for the examples of good traits we see.

Psalm 146:3—Parents should not depend on the state for training their children. Parents have the responsibility for training their children. If the state does anything that helps this, so much the better; but parents need to be aware of things the state (or public schools) might do that would negatively affect the parents' training.

Lesson 119

1. The GI Bill (of Rights)
2. The Baby Boom
3. Falling value of the dollar and rising prices
4. People were ready to spend, businesses wanted more profit, and workers demanded more pay.
5. He appointed the first Civil Rights Commission and other groups; he forbade discrimination in Federal hiring and ordered the military to be desegregated.
6. Jackie Robinson
7. Republican
8. The Do-Nothing Congress
9. Republican candidate Thomas Dewey
10. The Fair Deal

Questions on Harry S. Truman's Farewell Address

1. Making decisions
2. Across the street from the White House in Blair House
3. The Cold War
4. Sending troops to Korea
5. Yes

Bible Question

Advantages: ability to worship and teach as we see fit without persecution; disadvantages: can get comfortable in our freedom and take it for granted, might not have a strong faith if it is dependent on religious freedom provided by the government

Lesson 120

1. Genesis 17:8 and the promise of restoration after the Babylonian captivity
2. Ishmael
3. Islam
4. Zionism
5. Great Britain
6. May 14, 1948
7. To attack Israel
8. Refusing to salute the U.S. flag

9. That it was constitutional
10. If the instruction took place off school grounds and received no help from the school district.

History Quiz on Unit 24

1. b; 2. d; 3. d; 4. a; 5. b; 6. c; 7. c; 8. a; 9. a; 10. b; 11. c; 12. b; 13. a; 14. a; 15. d

Unit 25

Lesson 121

1. Adlai Stevenson
2. Robert A. Taft
3. The existence of and Nixon's access to a political "slush fund"
4. By the people's responses to him sent to the Republican National Committee
5. Alaska and Hawaii
6. The Interstate Highway System
7. Organized crime, especially with regard to labor unions
8. AFL and CIO
9. His heart attack
10. Estes Kefauver

Bible Question

Luke 12:48—We have been entrusted with greater prosperity, health, and educational opportunities, and greater ability for communication and travel. We need to use these well for the Lord.

Lesson 122

1. *Plessy v. Ferguson* (1896)
2. Separate facilities were almost never equal; and separation itself was an insult to them.
3. That separate facilities were inherently unequal
4. By resisting the call to integrate schools
5. He called out the National Guard
6. White Citizens Councils
7. Rosa Parks
8. A court ruled that segregation on city buses was unconstitutional.
9. Voting rights
10. Residential patterns and public attitudes

Questions on *Brown v. Board of Education*

1. Kansas, South Carolina, Virginia, Delaware
2. The equal protection clause of the Fourteenth

Amendment

3. The importance of public education

4. It gives them a sense of inferiority and has a detrimental effect.

5. The complexity of implementing changes in public schools as a result of the decision.

Lesson 123

1. Nikita Khrushchev

2. For the U.S. and U.S.S.R. to exchange military information and to allow air photography of military installations

3. A sometimes heated discussion between Khrushchev and Vice President Nixon at a display of a modern American kitchen in Moscow in 1959

4. The Russians shooting down an American U-2 spy plane

5. Hungary

6. Egypt

7. Lebanon

8. France

9. Ho Chi Minh

10. The 17th parallel

Bible Question

1 Timothy 2:9-10—People often want to be liked and accepted by their peers, so they try to conform to their peers' speech and habits, the way they dress, the clothes they wear, the kinds of houses in which they live, the cars they drive, and so forth. The world tempts us to follow its ways because it looks successful.

Lesson 124

1. The Russian launch of the Sputnik on October 4, 1957

2. It caused Americans to question their assumed superiority in technology, space science, and military preparedness.

3. A dog

4. January 31, 1958

5. Hitting the moon with an unmanned satellite (1959) and sending a man into orbit around the earth (1961)

6. National Aeronautics and Space Administration (NASA)

7. Inter-continental ballistic missile

8. First-strike and responding with total destruction

9. North American Air Defense, a radar system that kept watch for incoming missiles over the North Pole

10. Public education, especially in teaching math, science, and foreign languages

Questions on Dwight D. Eisenhower's Farewell Address

1. He thought that there had been good cooperation.

2. The creation of a permanent armaments industry

3. The net income of all U.S. corporations

4. The military-industrial complex

5. A scientific-technological elite

Bible Questions

Challenges: Opposing false teachers, challenging the predominant lifestyle on Crete, the temptation that people faced to continue living this way when they became Christians; other answers possible. Emphases: Titus needed to emphasize the transforming power of grace, self-discipline, godly living, and "loving what is good."

Lesson 125

1. Home construction

2. The South and Southwest (the Sunbelt)

3. It increased.

4. "Under God" in the Pledge of Allegiance and "In God We Trust" as the national motto

5. *The Robe, The Ten Commandments,* and *Ben-Hur*

6. Television

7. Rock and roll

8. Materialism

9. The increase in church membership was not the same as an increase in discipleship, people often joined churches to blend in with society, a greater emphasis on positive Christian attitudes and cultural Christianity, and many rabid segregationists were church-goers.

10. Separate from and in rebellion against the adult generation

History Quiz on Unit 25

1. R; 2. T; 3. P; 4. B; 5. S; 6. O; 7. Q; 8. C; 9. N; 10. D; 11. H; 12. G; 13. L; 14. I; 15. E; 16. K; 17. J; 18. F; 19. M; 20. A

History Test on Units 21-25

I. Write a brief paragraph explaining each of the following.

1. Prohibition—Outlawing of the manufacture and sale of intoxicating beverages. U.S. policy during the 1920s. Widely ignored. Illegal sale carried on by organized crime. Ended under Roosevelt.

2. WPA (Works Progress Administration)—New Deal program that gave work to many people. Jobs included construction projects; artistic projects also funded.

3. Social Security—New Deal program that provided unemployment, disability, and retirement benefits. Funded by taxes.

4. Berlin Airlift—When Soviets blocked land access to West Berlin, U.S. airlifted food, fuel, and other supplies to the city for almost a year, 1948-1949. Soviets eventually backed down and re-opened the road.

5. GI Bill—Law passed by Congress after World War II that provided medical, educational, housing and other benefits to veterans.

6. Marshall Plan—Developed by Secretary of State George Marshall to help European countries rebuild after World War II. Prevented rise of new dictators and lessened Communist influence in western Europe.

7. Cold War—Tense standoff between the U.S. and the U.S.S.R. The two countries never fought each other directly, but the arms buildup by both nations increased tensions and the fear of a nuclear war. Both nations sought to influence other countries to be their allies.

8. Battle of Britain—German bombing of the island of Great Britain during World War II and the resistance by the RAF and the British people. The bombing was carried out in anticipation of a German invasion of Britain, but British resistance was so strong and German losses so great that the invasion was called off.

9. *Brown v. Board of Education*—1954 U.S. Supreme Court decision that declared segregation in public schools to be unconstitutional. This was a landmark decision that recognized the inequality of educational opportunities for blacks and the need for greater civil rights for blacks. Implementation was slowed by white resistance to the decision, especially in the South.

10. Sputnik—First man-made satellite to orbit the earth. Launched by the Soviet Union in 1957, it was a matter of concern to the U.S. because it indicated that the Communists were ahead of the U.S. in space technology. The U.S. responded with its own satellite the next year, the formation of NASA, and increased Federal funding for science education.

II. Matching

1. B; 2. J; 3. E; 4. F; 5. C; 6. M; 7. L; 8. O; 9. N; 10. K; 11. I; 12. G; 13. A; 14. D; 15. H

III. Korean War—Summary should include: At the end of World War II, Communists controlled North Korea and the U.S. controlled the south. In 1950 Communist North Korean troops invaded South Korea and pushed U.S. and South Korean forces to the southern tip of the peninsula. The U.N. called for help to repel the invasion. Allied forces led by Douglas MacArthur landed at Inchon and cut the supply lines of the Communists troops. The Allied forces pushed the Communists back to the Chinese border, but then Chinese troops invaded and pushed the Allies back to about the 38th parallel. Keeping South Korea free became the official American policy, but it was difficult for many Americans to accept the idea of a limited war. MacArthur wanted to bomb areas of China and use Taiwanese troops, but Truman resisted. When MacArthur publicly differed with Administration policy, Truman fired MacArthur. A cease-fire was finally declared in 1953, but no official peace agreement has been reached.

IV. Presidents: Washington, John Adams, Jefferson, Madison, Monroe, John Quincy Adams, Jackson, Van Buren, William Henry Harrison, Tyler, Polk, Taylor, Fillmore, Pierce, Buchanan, Lincoln, Andrew Johnson, Grant, Hayes, Garfield, Arthur, Cleveland, Benjamin Harrison, Cleveland, McKinley, Theodore Roosevelt, Taft, Wilson, Harding, Coolidge, Hoover, Franklin Roosevelt, Truman, Eisenhower

English Test for Units 21-25

Paper comparing *Christy* and *To Kill a Mockingbird* (*TKAM*)—Answers might include the following points: (1) Similarities and differences: Both are set in the rural South in the early 1900s, both were written by women, both have female central characters, both are about realizations learned. *Christy* is about Appalachian mountain people, *TKAM* is about a small town in Alabama. The issue of race is more prominent in *TKAM*. (2) The influence of prejudice in each setting: Many of the people in *Christy* are prejudiced against outsiders, many of the whites in *TKAM* are prejudiced against blacks. (3) The roles of men and women in each setting: In *Christy* the men are often detached from their families and sometimes are rebels against society. The women are stronger characters and maintain the home. Dr. MacNeill is a strong male figure. In *TKAM* some of the women in the town are keepers of tradition; the Finch family is affected by the absence of a mother; Atticus Finch is a strong male figure. (4) The significance of Christianity in each story: The Christians in *Christy* are connected with the mission and are seen with suspicion by some of the mountain people; Christianity is seen in how people treat each other. In *TKAM* there is little overt Christian influence, although Atticus is living out his faith by defending the black man Tom Robinson. (5) What you learned by reading each book: Responses will vary.

Bible Test for Units 21-25

This test consists of five one-paragraph answers. Answers should be graded on the basis of how well the student grasps the spiritual issues involved with each topic.

Unit 26

Lesson 126

1. Democrat: John F. Kennedy; Republican: Richard Nixon
2. Nixon
3. The televised debates between the candidates
4. The New Frontier
5. Resistance to Kennedy's program by southern Democrats
6. The Bay of Pigs
7. "Ich bin ein Berliner" ("I am a Berliner")

8. High altitude photography
9. The Soviet Union agreed to remove the missiles and not build any in Cuba, and the U.S. agreed not to try another invasion of Cuba. The U.S. also removed some missiles in Turkey and Europe.
10. Lee Harvey Oswald

Questions on John F. Kennedy's Inaugural Address

1. A new generation of Americans
2. We shall pay any price, bear any burden, meet any hardship, support any friend, and oppose any foe.
3. If a free society cannot help the many who are poor, it cannot save the few who are rich.
4. This hemisphere intends to remain the master of its own house.
5. Ask not what your country can do for you; ask what you can do for your country.

Bible Question

Luke 4:18-19—He saw His mission as reaching out to the weak, the have-nots, and the people that society rejected.

Lesson 127

1. Lyndon Johnson
2. Texas
3. The Great Society
4. The Civil Rights Act and the Voting Rights Act
5. The War on Poverty
6. Medicare and Medicaid
7. Barry Goldwater
8. That the party had been controlled by an Eastern liberal establishment
9. Giving the District of Columbia three electoral votes, outlawing the poll tax, and presidential succession
10. Legislative reapportionment, the rights of accused persons, and mandatory school prayer and Bible reading

Questions on "Our God, He Is Alive"

1. Scientist
2. To the prophets and through His word
3. Mortal mind

Bible Questions

Luke 6:1-11—Jesus challenged their attitudes, their teachings, their religious system, and their position of power. He might challenge today's leaders on their wealth and worldly lifestyles, divisions within Christendom, the focus on church finances, and the lack of concern for the poor. Other answers possible.

Lesson 128

1. Sit-ins
2. The University of Mississippi and the University of Alabama
3. Birmingham, Alabama
4. The March on Washington civil rights demonstration in August of 1963
5. Rioting by blacks
6. Viet Cong
7. The Gulf of Tonkin resolution
8. Fear of the Soviet Union or China increasing its involvement in the war
9. It was weak and corrupt and the South Vietnamese army was not strong or well-trained.
10. Aerial bombing

Questions on "Letter from a Birmingham Jail" and the "I Have a Dream" Speech

1. An open letter from white clergymen calling the demonstrations "unwise and untimely"
2. He said that his group had a chapter in Birmingham and that he had been asked to come.
3. Collection of the facts to determine whether injustices exist, negotiation, self-purification, and direct action
4. A just law is a man-made code that squares with the moral law or the law of God. An unjust law is a code that is out of harmony with the moral law.
5. White moderates and the church
6. 100 years
7. From the quicksands of racial injustice to the solid rock of brotherhood
8. Until the Negro is granted his citizenship rights
9. That one day the sons of former slaves and the sons of former slaveowners would be able to sit down together at the table of brotherhood
10. "Free at last, free at last. Thank God Almighty, we are free at last."

Bible Question

Various answers possible. Answers might include the poor, the uneducated, the handicapped, the immigrant, and the Muslim.

Lesson 129

1. An intelligence-gathering ship captured by North Korea in 1968
2. It turned people against the war.
3. Eugene McCarthy
4. That he was seeking peace in Vietnam and that he would not run for re-election
5. Memphis, Tennessee
6. The California primary
7. The police and demonstrators
8. Hubert Humphrey
9. George Wallace
10. Richard Nixon

Bible Question

An attitude of repentance would prevent many interpersonal confrontations and judgmental attitudes toward others. People would be more sympathetic toward what others were going through. Other answers possible.

Lesson 130

1. Music
2. The Jews had spread belief in God, Greek had become a world language, and the Roman Empire provided a relatively peaceful world in the Mediterranean region.
3. He told the Jewish leaders how they were wrong and called them hypocrites.
4. He showed the value of the individual, he redefined what it means to be male and female, and he had a great respect for marriage and children.
5. Involvement in reform movements such as abolition of slavery and prohibition, building hospitals and providing medical care, encouraging education
6. Believers have done some cruel things in the name of Jesus; Christianity in Europe is largely a dead faith; denominational divisions have turned many people off.
7. He had words of praise for non-Israelites, women, tax collectors, "sinners," and others not acceptable to the Jews; He noticed people that others did not care about; He blessed the poor

and warned the rich.
8. Answers will vary.
9. Answers will vary.
10. Answers will vary.

History Quiz on Unit 26

1. H; 2. D; 3. O; 4. M; 5. I; 6. K; 7. C; 8. N; 9. E; 10. A; 11. F; 12. B; 13. G; 14. J; 15. L

Unit 27

Lesson 131

1. Continue the peace negotiations, Vietnamize the war, bomb Communist sites in Cambodia
2. Kent State University
3. Secret Pentagon documents leaked to the press by Daniel Ellsberg
4. The Communists launched a full scale attack.
5. Poor planning, no strategy for victory, unreliable South Vietnamese army, committed enemy
6. Busing
7. A proposed Constitutional amendment forbidding discrimination on the basis of sex. It never became part of the Constitution.
8. OPEC
9. Visiting Communist China and the Soviet Union
10. Detente

Questions on "Confessions of a Baby Boomer"

1. When the author was four years old
2. Two sons
3. *Exploring*
4. The South
5. In the late 1960s, when he was in high school

Questions on "A Day in July"

1. Man landing on the moon
2. A comparison between the manned spacecraft and the moon as earth's satellite
3. They had been separate, but now they were connected by the manned landing.

Bible Question

Psalm 139:13-16—The unborn child is created by God, is precious in His sight, and is known intimately by Him.

Lesson 132

1. He was shot and paralyzed by a gunman in Laurel, MD.
2. George McGovern
3. Thomas Eagleton was found to have received psychiatric treatment, so he was replaced by Sargent Shriver.
4. Employees of the Committee to Re-Elect the President were arrested for breaking into the offices of the Democratic National Committee.
5. "What did the President know and when did he know it?"
6. A secret recording system
7. He pleased no contest to a charge of tax evasion and resigned.
8. He participated in the cover-up of the Watergate scandal and obstructed its investigation.
9. The House Judiciary Committee had approved three articles of impeachment, and the House was about to take up the matter to vote on the articles.
10. He pardoned Nixon for any crimes he might have committed while President.

Questions on Gerald R. Ford's Remarks at His Swearing-In

1. With their prayers
2. By any secret promises
3. Our long national nightmare
4. A government of laws and not of men
5. For Nixon and his family

Bible Question

Luke 1:41—According to the Bible, an unborn child is a baby, a person.

Lesson 133

1. Minority leader in the House
2. Recovery from Watergate scandal, poor economy, fall of Vietnam
3. Bob Dole
4. Jimmy Carter
5. Governor of Georgia
6. Resentment against the Republicans for Nixon and Watergate
7. Inflation, high interest rates, unemployment, higher fuel costs
8. The Camp David agreement between Israel and Egypt

9. Cutting grain shipments to Russia, boycotting the Moscow Olympics
10. The Iran hostage crisis

Bible Question

Exodus 4:11—This verse says that the unborn child and the child's physical abilities are created by God.

Lesson 134

1. The Iran hostage crisis
2. America's support of Israel and the immoral material produced in the U.S. and distributed to other countries
3. He limited foreign aid to countries with poor human rights records.
4. The U.S. has boycotted Cuba to try to influence a change of government there, but the U.S. wants to influence Chinese policies by developing close economic ties with China.
5. We have trade with them even though they persecute Christians and have people work in poor conditions for low pay.
6. The Unification Church
7. The People's Temple in Jonestown, Guyana.
8. The 1978 Harvard commencement exercise
9. A loss of courage, using freedom to promote evil, criticism of the press, crisis of the spirit brought about by material abundance
10. Whether the world is better by a person's life

Bible Question

More interest in profits than in treating people right, departure from God's Word with the development of cults, the failings listed by Solzhenitsyn

Lesson 135

1. Nineteenth century
2. A Texas woman who was not able to obtain an abortion. A suit was filed on her behalf.
3. Abortion had to be available before viability, but it could be regulated after that point.
4. Pharmakeia
5. Is the unborn a person, who has the right to equal protection under the law?
6. That they are created by God and are seen as persons.
7. The unborn Jesus and John the Baptist are

called babies.
8. They believed that abortion was wrong.
9. The Hippocratic oath, statements of nineteenth century feminists, opinions of medical and scientific experts
10. Oppose funding for it and candidates who support it, be willing to adopt or support adoption, teach people about Jesus so their lives and hearts will change; other ideas possible.

Questions on *Roe v. Wade*

1. The delicate and controversial nature of the issue
2. The right of privacy
3. Viability of the fetus
4. The trimesters of a pregnancy
5. There was no indication of wrong in Roe's first trimester, the case did not involve a violation of privacy, and he thought it was wrong to strike down the entire Texas law.

Questions on "In America"

1. 3,000
2. To make up what is real, to say just what we feel, and to kill an unborn child
3. Jesus came as a baby in the womb.
4. A mother chose life for her baby.

Questions on *The Giver*

1. This was when life assignments were given.
2. That he could lie
3. Sameness
4. Grandparents were there, love was present
5. To kill or euthanize
6. To help things change, to share memories with the people
7. People lose a sense of direction and can be easily led; other answers possible.
8. People cannot be trusted.
9. Knowledge of the past helps guide what we do in the future; other answers possible.
10. We learn how to help others, we see what is important in life, we see the consequences of our actions; other answers possible.
11. Abortion, physician-assisted suicide, lack of knowledge of history; other answers possible
12. Life and people have less value and meaning; other answers possible
13. Various answers possible

History Quiz on Unit 27

1. c; 2. d; 3. d; 4. c; 5. c; 6. d; 7. a; 8. b; 9. a; 10. b; 11. b; 12. c; 13. d; 14. d; 15. a

Unit 28

Lesson 136

1. Actor
2. Governor of California
3. Jimmy Carter
4. "Are you better off now than you were four years ago?"
5. Moral Majority
6. He fired the air traffic controllers and had new ones trained.
7. It began running huge deficits.
8. 508 points of the Dow Jones average, or 22% of its value
9. Space Shuttle
10. Acquired Immune Deficiency Syndrome
11. Walter Mondale

Questions on Ronald Reagan's First Inaugural Address

1. Government
2. We are a nation that has a government—not the other way around.
3. He did not believe in a fate that would happen "no matter what we do," but he did "believe in a fate that will fall on us if we do nothing."
4. The will and moral courage of free men and women
5. Martin Treptow

Bible Question

Philippians 1:12-18—Paul was in prison, and his imprisonment for the gospel had become known throughout the praetorian guard and to everyone else. In addition, others were emboldened to speak the word of God without fear. Some preached out of poor motives, but at least Christ was proclaimed.

Lesson 137

1. An evil empire
2. Solidarity
3. Strategic Defense Initiative ("Star Wars")
4. The elimination of a complete class of weapons, intermediate nuclear missiles
5. Tear down the Berlin Wall
6. As part of a peace-keeping force
7. Grenada
8. The Iran-Contra scandal
9. People in the U.S. government secretly sold arms to Iran in the hope that Iran could influence the release of American hostages in Lebanon. Some of the profits from the arms sales were sent to the Contras in Nicaragua who were fighting the Communist government there.
10. Oliver North

Questions on Ronald Reagan's Farewell Address

1. Freedom man
2. 19 million
3. The Soviet Union
4. The deficit
5. John Winthrop

Bible Question

Philippians 1:18-21—Answers will vary.

Lesson 138

1. George Bush (Republican), Michael Dukakis (Democrat)
2. Congressman, U.N. ambassador, liaison to China, chairman of the Republican National Committee, director of the CIA
3. Savings and loan
4. To raise taxes and cut spending
5. That he would agree to no new taxes
6. Clarence Thomas
7. Law professor Anita Hill
8. Panama
9. Mikhail Gorbachev
10. The Berlin Wall was torn down.
11. Commonwealth of Independent States

Bible Questions

Philippians 1:22-26—Paul knew that he would either be released or be executed. He preferred to depart and be with Christ, but he believed that he would be released. This would mean that he would be able to come to the Philippians and continue his ministry.

Lesson 139

1. Iraq invaded Kuwait.
2. It condemned the aggression and approved the use of force to repel Iraq.
3. Operation Desert Shield/Desert Storm
4. Colin Powell
5. Norman Schwarzkopf
6. Air and missile attacks on Iraq
7. 100 hours
8. Iraq was to pay reparations to Kuwait, destroy its chemical and biological weapons and allow for international inspection, and respect no-fly zones over the country.
9. It demonstrated the advanced state of American military technology.
10. Bush received unprecedented job approval ratings.

Bible Questions

Philippians 2:1-15—(1) Answers will vary. (2) Complaining says that you don't trust God in circumstances that you don't like. (3) Answers will vary.

Lesson 140

1. He brought Joseph to a position of power and saved his family's lives.
2. He brought salvation out of the cruel and unjust death of Christ.
3. The missionary impulse that followed the war
4. It served to advance the gospel.
5. Despite their motives, Christ was proclaimed.
6. He would get out either by being released or by being executed.
7. To live is Christ and to die is gain.
8. Attitude

History Quiz on Unit 28

1. G; 2. B; 3. F; 4. E; 5. C; 6. A; 7. D; 8. a; 9. c; 10. d; 11. d; 12. c; 13. b; 14. a; 15. b

Unit 29

Lesson 141

1. The economy
2. Arkansas
3. Tennessee Senator Albert Gore Jr.
4. H. Ross Perot

5. Republican Contract With America
6. Republicans gained control of the House and Senate; first time sine 1952
7. North American Free Trade Agreement, creating a free-trade zone among the U.S., Mexico, and Canada.
8. Bob Dole
9. Dow Jones Industrial Average, an index of stock values based on the stock of 30 large companies
10. The Federal Reserve Board, which guides monetary policy for the U.S. government.

Questions on the Republican Contract with America

1. Republicans running for election to the U.S. House in 1994
2. On the first day of the 104th Congress
3. To require all laws that apply to the rest of the country also apply equally to the Congress
4. A balanced budget/tax limitation amendment and a legislative line-item veto

Bible Question

2 Samuel 11-12—David committed adultery, he had Uriah killed, and he tried to cover up his wrongs. He recovered when he confessed his wrongs and repented of them.

Lesson 142

1. Latin America
2. Asians
3. Assimilating them into society, education and social services for them; how they should be registered and pay taxes
4. The Branch Davidians
5. The bombing of the Murrah Federal Building in Oklahoma City
6. School shootings
7. 1944
8. They are able to perform so many different functions
9. A network of networks that provides e-mail, information, and business communication among computers
10. Telephone lines

Questions on "Defense of Conservatism"

1. The National Bar Association
2. The assassination of Dr. Martin Luther King Jr.

3. Civility
4. The virtual isolation he felt, even within the Court
5. The tendency to personalize differences
6. Anger
7. He takes conservative positions that are unusual among blacks.
8. His right to think for himself

Bible Questions

Romans 7:14-25—Answers will vary. Romans 8:1—The answer is that there is no condemnation for those who are in Christ Jesus.

Lesson 143

1. Somalia
2. Jean-Bertrand Aristide
3. The proposal that Israel agree to give the Palestinians control of land and that the Palestinians agree not to attack Israel
4. Jordan
5. Yitzhak Rabin
6. Yugoslavia
7. Slobodan Milosevic
8. Kosovo
9. Albanian Muslims
10. NATO

Bible Question

1 Timothy 1:12-16—God accepts us by His grace when we trust in him, despite our failings. God even puts us into His service, even though we had failed Him!

Lesson 144

1. Whitewater
2. Paula Jones
3. It was settled in November of 1998 when Clinton agreed to pay Jones $850,000 but without any admission or apology.
4. Monica Lewinsky
5. He denied them.
6. In August of 1998 in grand jury testimony and in a speech to the American people
7. Perjury and obstruction of justice
8. Both articles failed to receive the necessary two-thirds majority.
9. Clinton admitted that he had lied under oath, he paid a $25,000 fine, and he had his law license

suspended for five years; in return, Clinton would not be prosecuted after leaving office.
10. Answers may vary.

Bible Question

We respect Peter despite his failings because he repented of his sins and because his basic stance was one of faith in Christ despite his failings. Peter did not let his failings define him. Instead, he let Christ change him.

Lesson 145

1. Bill Clinton, Richard Nixon, Jesse Jackson, and Newt Gingrich
2. Imperfect
3. Our perception becomes clouded; we might think that it is acceptable for us to commit wrong; we might use a double standard; we might think that some sins are worse than others.
4. To treat that person the way you want to be treated
5. To make sure that his or her own life is right before God.
6. To make sure that his or her influence on others is good.
7. God
8. To be rid of everything, including thoughts, that cause you to sin, even if they are very much a part of your life and even if society thinks you are strange for getting rid of them.

History Quiz on Unit 29

1. E; 2. I; 3. K; 4. J; 5. A; 6. N; 7. D; 8. M; 9. G; 10. B; 11. H; 12. C; 13. F; 14. L; 15. P; 16. S; 17. T; 18. O; 19. Q; 20. R

Unit 30

Lesson 146

1. 281,421,906
2. 13.2%
3. California
4. New York City
5. 77.9 years
6. 28 million
7. 105.5 million
8. Almost ten trillion dollars
9. The Roman Catholic Church
10. Southern Baptist Convention
11. 5.8 million

Bible Question

Romans 8:18-25—Answers will vary, but might include persecution of Christians, physical suffering, and the turn by much of society against Christianity.

Lesson 147

1. Democrats: Al Gore; Republicans: George Bush
2. Joseph Lieberman was the first major party candidate for national office who was Jewish.
3. Richard Cheney
4. Florida
5. The U. S. Supreme Court
6. Gore
7. Bush won 271 to 266
8. Gore won New England, the large industrial states, and the urban counties; Bush won most of the South and Midwest.

Bible Question

Answers will vary.

Lesson 148

1. Four
2. World Trade Center
3. Pentagon
4. Passengers attacked the hijackers, and the plane went down in Pennsylvania.
5. Osama bin Laden
6. Afghanistan
7. They launched an attack on al-Qaeda terrorist sites and the Taliban government of Afghanistan.
8. Iraq
9. Saddam Hussein
10. Spain and Great Britain

Questions on the "Address to a Joint Session of Congress and the American People"

1. Todd Beamer
2. $40 billion
3. Office of Homeland Security
4. A protracted war, occurring in many different places, sometimes with covert actions
5. George Howard

Bible Question

Answers will vary.

Lesson 149

1. Colin Powell, Condoleezza Rice
2. China
3. A sizeable tax cut
4. A campaign finance reform law
5. It had increasing deficits each year.
6. Republican
7. Hurricane Katrina
8. John Roberts and Samuel Alito
9. The Democrats gained control of both houses of Congress.
10. Nancy Pelosi, the first woman to hold this position

Bible Question

Answers will vary.

Lesson 150

1. Religion
2. Abortion, euthanasia, pornography, physical and sexual abuse, etc.
3. Visit another country
4. We still share the same basic ideals and principles that were believed when the country was founded.
5. The way we select representatives, who can vote, the size and influence of the Federal government, the role of political parties
6. Urban
7. Being admired for who we are
8. People have not decided to make their families strong; families are influenced by the world; both men and women work outside of the home and fill their lives with many activities away from the home.
9. The threat of terrorism
10. The perspective of faith

History Quiz on Unit 30

1. 75% white
2. California
3. Los Angeles
4. Eighty percent
5. Ten trillion dollars
6. Roman Catholic Church
7. Al Gore
8. Florida
9. The U.S. Supreme Court
10. Four passenger planes

11. Pentagon
12. Osama bin Laden
13. Afghanistan
14. Iraq
15. Colin Powell
16. John Kerry
17. Katrina
18. John Roberts
19. Democrats
20. Nancy Pelosi

History Test on Units 26-30

1. d; 2. b; 3. b; 4. c; 5. a; 6. c; 7. b; 8. a; 9. b; 10. c; 11. c; 12. a; 13. c; 14. d; 15. a; 16. a; 17. c; 18. b; 19. b; 20. d; 21. d; 22. a; 23. b; 24. d; 25. d; 26. a; 27. c; 28. a; 29. d; 30. a; 31. c; 32. b; 33. a; 34. D; 35. F; 36. A; 37. E; 38. G; 39. B; 40. C;
41. Presidents: Washington, John Adams, Jefferson, Madison, Monroe, John Quincy Adams, Jackson, Van Buren, William Henry Harrison, Tyler, Polk, Taylor, Fillmore, Pierce, Buchanan, Lincoln, Andrew Johnson, Grant, Hayes, Garfield, Arthur, Cleveland, Benjamin Harrison, Cleveland, McKinley, Theodore Roosevelt, Taft, Wilson, Harding, Coolidge, Hoover, Franklin Roosevelt, Truman, Eisenhower, Kennedy, Lyndon Johnson, Nixon, Ford, Carter, Reagan, George H. W. Bush, Clinton, George W. Bush

English Test on Units 26-30

1. a; 2. c; 3. b; 4. Answers will vary; 5. Man landing on the moon
6. Possible ideas to look for in answers:

a. Descriptions of South in *Uncle Tom's Cabin* and *To Kill a Mockingbird*: In *Uncle Tom's Cabin*, blacks were legally subservient to whites, while in *To Kill a Mockingbird* blacks were socially subservient to whites. Most of the whites in both books saw themselves as superior to blacks. The outlook for blacks in both books was bleak. Atticus Finch was a notable exception in his attitude toward blacks.

b. Moral failures in *The Scarlet Letter* and *To Kill a Mockingbird*: Hester's moral failure is obvious and roundly condemned. The failures of the town leaders and of Dimmesdale in terms of judgmentalism and honesty were also real but were not acknowledged. Hester's efforts to rear Pearl was an attempt to redeem the girls' life. Hester and Arthur wanted to leave to start life over again, but they had not addressed their sin honestly with the community and therefore failed. Atticus Finch tried to redeem Tom Robinson's reputation. He was not able to do that, but he helped redeem Boo Radley's reputation with his children.

c. Family dynamics in *Little Women* and *Mama's Bank Account*: In each book, the mother is the strong, dominant parent, even though the wife respects her husband in each case. This is probably because each book is written from the perspective of the daughter or daughters. The children are generally respectful of their parents, although in *Little Women* they are portrayed as having more independent thoughts. Parent-child interaction is generally positive and healthy and often involves the parents teaching the children about life.

d. Settings of the rural South in *Narrative of the Life of David Crockett* and *Christy*: In both books, the characters are in something of a battle with nature and have to cope with the elements. Native Americans are the primary enemy for David Crockett, while outsiders are seen with suspicion in *Christy*.

Bible Test on Units 26-30

1. d; 2. c; 3. d; 4. a; 5. b; 6. a; 7. c; 8. b; 9. d; 10. b
11. Jesus condemned the hypocrisy and faithless traditions of the religious leaders and their grip on the spiritual lives of the people. They had elevated their traditions to the level of the doctrines of God. Jesus honored many who were looked down upon socially in His day, such as women, the handicapped, Gentiles, and those who were seen as "sinners."
12. Answers will vary, but should include these ideas: All have sinned, but this does not mean that we should turn a blind eye to sin in the lives of leaders or of ourselves. We should expect integrity in public leaders. Each person answers to God for our lives, but we should be aware of our influence on others.

Teaching the Heart, Soul, and Mind

Notgrass company

www.notgrass.com ★ 1-800-211-8793

History & Government

Exploring America Curriculum Package by Ray Notgrass — 89.95
This curriculum takes students from European exploration of America to the war in Iraq. It includes the history narrative, Bible lessons, and reading and writing assignments needed to complete one high school credit each in Bible, American History, and English. *High School.*

Exploring America Quiz & Exam Pack — 14.95
Optional review questions, quizzes, tests, and answer keys.

Exploring World History Curriculum Package by the Notgrass Family — 89.95
This curriculum surveys world history from Creation to modern times. It includes the history narrative, Bible lessons, and reading and writing assignments needed to earn one year's credit in Bible, World History, and English. *High School.*

Exploring World History Quiz & Exam Book — 14.95
Optional review questions, quizzes, tests, and answer keys.

Exploring Government Curriculum Package by Ray Notgrass — 49.95
A complete, one-semester study of American Federal, state, and local government, with special emphasis on the U.S. Constitution. Package includes a collection of historical documents, speeches, and essays. *High School.*

Exploring Government Quiz & Exam Pack — 7.95
Optional review questions, quizzes, tests, and answer keys.

Exploring Tennessee and **Exploring Georgia** by the Notgrass Family — 59.95 each
Each of our state history packages contains four components: a book of history lessons (150 for TN, 75 for GA), a student workbook with activities, a field trip guide to each county of the state, and a Quiz & Exam Pack. *Ages 9-14.*

Additional Student Workbook — 14.95
Additional Quiz & Exam Pack — 3.95

First-Person History by John Notgrass
First-person dramatizations about real people from history. *Ages 8 and up.*

CD __ Building a Kingdom: King Alfred of the West Saxons (848-899 in England) — 6.00 each
CD __ Recollections of a Confederate Soldier: Sam Watkins of Tenn. (Civil War)

DVD __ One Soldier's Story: Wesley Biddle Notgrass (World War II) — 10.95

Record Keeping

Record of the Learning Lifestyle by Charlene Notgrass — 11.95 each
A simple and effective tool to help you maintain a record of your child's homeschooling. See at a glance what you are covering each week and feel good about what you are accomplishing. *Six different covers available. All ages.*

__ Basketball __ Cat __ Flower __ Horse __ Penguin __ Tree Frog

Unit Studies

Exploring the Library by Bethany Notgrass   9.95
Help your children discover the how, why, and joy of learning from a Biblical perspective. *Ages 8-14.*

Olympic Games by Charlene Notgrass   9.95
Learn physical education, history, geography, and Bible as you explore the ancient and modern Olympic Games. Illustrated with historic photographs. *Ages 8-14.*

Walking In Faith by Mary Evelyn Notgrass   9.95
A 30-lesson study of what the Bible says about faith. *Ages 8-14.*

Walking In Truth by Mary Evelyn Notgrass   9.95
A 30-lesson study of what the Bible says about truthfulness. *Ages 8-14.*

Celebrate Thanksgiving by Charlene Notgrass   9.95
Fifteen lessons about Thanksgiving history and traditions, craft ideas, scrapbook pages, and answer key. *Ages 8-14.*

Celebrate The Savior by Charlene Notgrass   9.95
Fifteen lessons about the birth and childhood of Jesus and Christmas celebrations through history and around the world. *Ages 8-14.*

Art

Draw to Learn the Book of Proverbs by Ray and Charlene Notgrass   14.95 each
Draw to Learn the Book of Acts by Mary Evelyn Notgrass
Draw to Learn the Book of Psalms by Charlene Notgrass
Draw to Learn the Life of Jesus by Charlene Notgrass
Draw to Learn the Letters of Paul by Ray and Charlene Notgrass
Children read a Bible passage, think about its meaning and about the drawing assignment, and draw a picture based on the passage. 150 lessons each. *All ages.*

Learn to Draw Second Edition by Mary Evelyn Notgrass   14.95
Drawing basics taught in 30 lessons, including lines and basic shapes, placement, size, overlapping, shadows, shading, horizon, coloring, and line direction. *Ages 10 and up.*

Family Resources

Daily Encouragement for Homeschooling Mothers   7.95
Written and Illustrated by Charlene Notgrass
A flip calendar you can use over and over to help you be successful in the role God has given you as a wife and mother. Thirty-one encouraging and practical ideas based on Titus 2.

Make It Your Ambition by John Notgrass   12.00
Encouraging young people to live for God's glory by examining what the Bible says about setting goals, managing finances, and preparing for marriage. *Ages 14 and up.*

Katy by Mary Evelyn Notgrass   7.50
Is it okay to be different? A delightful, touching, and humorous story about the summer a family decides to homeschool.

Historical Musical Drama DVDs Written and Directed by Mary Evelyn Notgrass   14.95 each
___ Sign of Love: Thomas Gallaudet and the Founding of the American School for the Deaf, 1817. *89 minutes. All ages.*
___ I Am Dreaming of America: Journey to Ellis Island, 1908. *84 minutes. All ages.*   39.95 for three
___ Yellow Star: Life in a Nazi-Occupied French Village, 1943. *88 minutes. All ages.*

Shipping (Media Mail: $2.95 up to $40 total, $4.95 for $40 and up; Priority Mail: $4.95 / $9.95)	
Subtotal	
Sales Tax (Add 9.75% in TN, 6.25% in IL, 7% in IN, 6% in PA, and your local rate in KS, MO, NC, OH, and TX. Customers in other states are responsible for applicable use taxes.)	
Total Due	

Order on-line at **notgrass.com**, call toll-free **1-800-211-8793**,
or indicate your selections and mail this form with your check or money order.

Send your order to this address:

Please allow two to four weeks (depending on your shipping choice) for orders sent to us by mail. Prices subject to change.

Notgrass Company
370 S. Lowe Ave., Suite A
PMB 211
Cookeville, TN 38501

E-mail Address

❑ Add me to your e-mail newsletter list.